A Power to Pivot Workbook

Connect You:

A Guide to Your Authentic Life

Set boundaries and empowered goals that support the best you that you can be! Put the pieces together and tap into your mindset, energy, and intuition to create more fun and flow in your life!

———————

Elizabeth A. Miles

Connect You: A Guide to Your Authentic Life; Set boundaries and empowered goals that support the best you that you can be! Put the pieces together and tap into your mindset, energy, and intuition to create more fun and flow in your life!

March Forth Media Company, Philadelphia, PA, www.MarchForthMediaCompany.com

Author: Elizabeth A. Miles

Editor: Elizabeth A. Miles & John P. Chapkovich

Cover Art: Elizabeth A. Miles, Abigail Miles, Mary E. Miles

Paperback ISBN: 978-1-7332829-9-4

E-book ISBN: 978-1-7332829-8-7

Amazon Paperback ISBN: 978-1-7332829-5-6

Disclaimer/Note: The contents of this book are intended for educational purposes only. The author of this book does not dispense or prescribe medical advice or medications or techniques, either directly or indirectly. No part of this book should be taken as such. This book is intended to be used as an aid to guide you in your life. If you feel you need additional support, either medically or physically, please consult your physician.

Dedication

JC: Love wins (always)! You really are Batman, and your wife really is always right.

Jess, Andy, Abby, Mary: You are four of the most beautiful people on the planet, and I value and love and respect each of you for keeping things real with me, always. Thank you for teaching me about humility, respect, courage, and love.

To You: Bring your light! Bring your love! To your journey, march forth.

Contents

Embrace the Now.................................1

Start Here, Begin Now!....................13

Making the Commitment.................15

Intentions...17

You: A Snapshot in Time... 21

Clarity: Who Are You and What Do You Want?....................................23

Activity: Current Self v. Future Self: A Visual..33

Authenticity.....................................35

What are you afraid of?...................37

Understanding Energy....................45

A Meditation: Feeling Into Your Energy..55

Energetic Blocks and Letting Go..61

Mindset..69

Types of Mindset............................73

Limiting Beliefs...............................79

Flipping the Script and Resetting the Mind...91

Activity: Reframing Limiting Beliefs..93

A Brief Intermission.......................97

Love, Yourself...............................101

Self-Acceptance: An Activity..........107

Forgiveness....................................113

Values and Boundaries and Priorities, Oh My!........................119

Confidence.....................................127

Ego v. Intuition: The Battle of the Ages..135

How to Listen to Your Intuition.139

Activity: Getting in Touch with Intuition..141

Activity: Seeking An Intuitive Answer...143

Another Intuitive Exercise............145

Activity: A Meditation.....................151

Manifestation, Co-Creation, and 153

Intuitive Goal-Setting....................153

6-Week Goals..................................155

6-Month Goals................................156

12-Month Goals..............................157

Alignment and Vision....................159

Activity: Create A Schedule for Success...163

Gratitude..169

Rewriting Your Story and Wrapping Things Up.......................171

Activity: A Letter to You.................177

Activity: Continuous Change.......179

Activity: A Letter for Acceptance 181

The End...183

Embrace the Now

Call it fate, or divine timing, or a stroke of luck. However you look at it, you and this book somehow found each other.

You don't need to be told you need or want to make a change in your life, nor do you need to be told how to do it. Intuitively, you know you have a choice, and, by the simple fact that you are here reading this book right now, you have already acknowledged that choice. You made the choice to go big, and to go better. To "level up" as the saying goes. You know, intuitively, that there is something more out there waiting for you. If not, you wouldn't be here.

Financially. Emotionally. Mentally. Physically. Spiritually. Which is it?

Which area of your life do you believe that, by changing even just *one* thing, you could and would make the biggest impact to improve your life?

Sadly, I am sorry to say, life doesn't work that way.

It's never just _one_ thing. It's never just _one_ aspect. We want to believe that the journey to create change in our lives is easy. The dirty little secret that nobody wants to talk about is: it's not.

It's also not hard.

It is, however, messy. It can be ugly and downright painful. There is no magical, perfect or straight path that we can walk to find ourselves in the place we want to be – making the money we want, in the career that we want, with the friends that we want, in a relationship that we want, etc., etc., etc. Life is a series of tests, obstacles, and lessons, all designed to help you understand yourself, get clarity on what you want, in order to make you uncomfortable. This forces you to do one of two things: stay where you are and hide, or move. The struggle to move forward happens when we avoid the mess, ignore the pain, and shove our discomfort down.

Let's face it: We want it to be easy.

Let me share a story with you.

One morning, I found myself laying in my bed, staring out my bedroom window. I was restless and anxious, and my legs kept thrashing around, almost uncontrollably. I felt hopeless and confused; empty and stuck. I felt paralyzed with my life. Wondering why I felt so bad, I realized I had been trying to run and hide my entire life. Running away, for me looked like this: blame, judging others, judging myself, shoving my thoughts and feelings down deeper, overeating, pushing or walking away from people in my life. I was fighting the same fight I had been fighting for years.

It was a mess. I was a mess. It hurt...bad!

Lying in bed that day, I had a vision. Maybe it was angel, maybe it was my Higher Self. Whomever it was, she said to me "hey...you know you can just step aside...stop fighting."

In that moment, I saw myself take a step towards that vision. My anxiety calmed a little, though not fully.

When the anxiety came back a few minutes later, this vision popped up again on the other side of me. "Now step here," she said. So, I did. I was getting out of the way of my fear, getting out of the way of any judgement or guilt or shame or obstacles. In the process, I was getting out of my own way as well.

As soon as I acknowledged this, my anxiety went away and I found a moment of peace. Suddenly, that tree outside of my window looked so much more vibrant and beautiful. It was gorgeous. The leaves were vibrant with red and orange hues. All I wanted to do was lay there and stare at that tree – which had been there all along.

In starting at the tree, I broke down and cried. I cried hard.

Feeling helpless. Broken. Alone. Trapped. I had to let myself feel that. Go there; go deep, in order to see the beauty that was right in front of me all along.

What changed? I changed.

I realized one thing…

I was spending so much time reliving the past – past failures, past mistakes, past hurt – that I was letting it impact my here and now.

Then, I realized that, by holding so tightly to the past, I let that be my story over and over and over again, defining my every action and decision, even in the now.

And here's another dirty little secret: we can't change the now. The "now" is only the "now" for this instant. You blink and that "now" is gone. Suddenly, quickly, the "now" is the past. The "now" cannot be destroyed or changed. It just keeps moving forward.

We spend so much time stuck in our past, desperately trying to control the now, believing that, by doing so, we will create a new outcome for our future. Instead of going within and learning new skills, instead of growing and evolving, and instead of allowing ourselves to hit that rock bottom, feeling the pain, and then standing up again to move forward, how often do we:

- Grab for the next drink?
- Go looking for the cake or cookie that will make us feel better?
- Punch and hit walls?
- Yell and scream?
- Isolate ourselves away from other people?
- Scramble to do whatever it takes to push that pain that we are in away, so that we can "live life to the fullest?"

We don't want to feel the pain of the past, which creates the same pain right here and now. We believe that mantras, affirmations, gratitude practices, etc. are going to get rid of our pain. They are a temporary fix – a band aid – to the problem. We keep running in circles. Instead of looking at the past for the lesson it can teach us and moving on, we hold onto the story as a way to define our existence. Things get uncomfortable, so we run and hide, saying "this is not what I want for the future." We get so focused on avoiding the pain, avoiding any failures or mistakes, trying to prove that it can't or won't happen again, and trying to prove that we are better than the situation presented. We believe that, if only we had "one more chance," somehow, we could change the outcome.

We let ourselves believe that if we could do it all over, that we'd do it differently.

You know your story all too well… inside out, forwards and backwards, upside down. Even though you want to prove that it won't or can't happen again, you continue to manifest the same issues in your life over and over and over again.

Because, in reality, it's not about changing it. You can't change the past. Ever!

Here's what you can do…learn from it. Feel it. Accept it. Right now! Then choose to walk away from it. It's there! It will always be there, but it does not need to define who you are or your existence.

I know that, for me, I didn't want to talk about the mess or the pain, or the fact that I was hurting or that I was struggling to find my way. I got so caught up in that, so much so that I tried to project what I believed was a picture-perfect life into the world. Deep down, I knew there was something bigger and better out there waiting for me, but I didn't value myself enough to know that I could make the choice to choose it for myself, and I didn't want anyone else to know that I needed help to see it either. I kept hiding, and running away from any and all situations that might involve discomfort and judgement, and hoping that someone else would rescue me from the hell that I felt like I was living.

It sucked! I didn't see myself, all of myself, for who I really was, and am, and I was too scared of sitting down and doing the work to truly figure it out.

I was told to do things like: go to the gym to lose weight...get a new job to make more money...go back to school to get to the next level...go to therapy to fix my emotional rollercoaster of a life. All of these "shoulds" were seemingly simple solutions that were "proven" to help me change my life in one way or another.

Guess what? They didn't work! I was spinning my wheels, feeling overwhelmed and confused without a clue how to move forward and find real success or change.

Because I kept telling myself the same story that got me there in the first place.

Why does this happen?

We are taught from a very young age:

➢ Don't ask questions.
➢ Don't question authority.
➢ Don't question your path to the future.
➢ Be innovative, but don't innovate too much, because going too far from the "norm" is bad.

We get the message from pretty early on to:

• Do what you are told.
• Do as I say, not as I do.
• Listen and don't ask questions.
• Just do what you need to survive.

How confusing, right? We hear a phrase as simple as "live for the now" and have to wonder "what the hell does that even mean?"

After all, how do you live for the now when you are taught:

➢ You can't ask questions?
➢ You can't question authority?
➢ You can't innovate or create too far from the norm because it makes others uncomfortable?

Society wants us to conform to a standard that keep us trapped living for a now that someone else decided was best or right for us. Because we get stuck in the cycle of trying to fight for our own identity and trying to stay in the "now" that the world wants you to believe is the best, right, safest place for you, we get stuck in a cycle of confusion, and end up scrambling through life, pushing our way through, without much real clarity on where we are going or why we are headed there. Unfortunately, and far too often, "live for the now" translates into this:

"I can do whatever the fuck I want right now, because, heck, I am only going to live once."

This creates the conditions for more blame and judgement, and showing up in the world more as a force of nature that is always ready to fight or flee, instead of showing up as a person who is capable of sitting and listening, truthfully, to the world inside and around you. It's not possible, from this headspace, to listen to your heart and know what you really want, or feel through situations and places to know if they are truly right for you. And, sadly, it's not possible to create the conditions in our relationships that foster open communication, compassion, and empathy...because you are constantly living with the battle in your head that causes you to switch between doing what you are told, and doing what you think you want to do to be happy.

In reality, the whole point is to envision the best and most amazing life you can for yourself, one that, in your heart of hearts, feels amazing for you...feels fun...feels free. One that you could and would commit to, because it's exciting, fulfilling, and creates the best version of yourself that could ever possibly present in this world. Then, plot your course, and take action, marching forward in that direction. That's it, one next step at a time. Don't get caught up in the past, or the now, or the future.

In reality, though, we have to do the work!

It's not just one thing. It's not just about intuition, or understanding mindset, or letting go of limiting beliefs. It's not just about setting goals and acting on them. It's not even just about saying affirmations and mantras, though they are important, too. Transformation encompasses each of these. It's like a puzzle. When you put all the pieces together, it makes you, and, hopefully lands you in a space where you respect, honor, and cherish each and every one of those pieces.

In this puzzle, each piece is like a puzzle unto itself. A little project. There is no one, single part that is more important than any other, and each one must be worked on in order for that bigger puzzle to be complete, in order for you to come to a better understanding of yourself, and in order for you to truly move into a life you love.

It is simple, but it is not easy, and it is not a one-and-done, now-move-on-to-the-next-piece kind of a project. I know! I tried that for most of my life. I would complete one project, and think "okay that's it – what's next?" I thought I did all that I needed to do, but I never really got anywhere.

It didn't matter how many awards I won. It didn't matter how many accomplishments I had on my resume, or promotions or raises I received. It didn't matter what kind of car I drove, or the brand of clothing I wore, or even which grocery store I shopped most often. I was hiding behind each of those as a way to validate who I was. They were just checkboxes. I hadn't truly learned anything, and I didn't find any real momentum in the direction I wanted to go until I got over myself, got real with myself, and embraced the mess that had become my life. Until I got comfortable with all of me – flaws and all – and embraced the fact that my life was a shit show, I would continue to tell myself the same story – I was the fat kid, the bad mom, an abused wife, the middle child – I could go on.

By holding onto this story, I kept looking at what everyone else was doing, and succeeding at, and then kept trying to fit myself into their process and system to get where I wanted to go. I was trying to fit myself into their box, into their story, their now, and wondering why it wasn't working for me.

Once I got tired of waiting for the next "thing" to come along, and tired of searching for answers that didn't feel right, and weren't working anyway, I realized that all of those stories I had been telling myself did NOT need to define me. They could just be stories.

This is when I started to understand energy and the laws of the universe. I began to understand intuition, and what my mindset sounded like. I came to understand that, every one of us has our own definitions for things like "success," "abundance," "leadership," "passion", and "creativity," but we don't allow ourselves to actually live in a way that aligns with our own, individual definitions. Instead, we let everyone else, society, our family of origin, our social media, etc., tell us what to do, who to be, and how to think.

You already know there is something bigger out there for you. That's why you are here. The longer it takes for you to ditch the story of your past, and the longer it takes for you to realize that you get to choose your path and need to stay focused on that path alone, not the past and not the future, the longer you will continue to live by everyone else's rulebook, denying yourself the pleasure and fun of living life on your own terms. You'll continue to devalue your thoughts, feelings, and emotions, while simultaneously trying to push and force yourself into the world in a way that leaves you controlling other people and situations, and feeling exhausted and disgusted with life in the process.

So, I ask you:

- ➢ What if you stopped fighting that voice inside of you, telling you to listen to the "shoulds" and "musts" from the world?
- ➢ What if you allowed yourself to embrace all of the parts of you that make you unique?
- ➢ What if you started to love who you were, even with the messiness life brings with it?
- ➢ Who could you become?
- ➢ What could you accomplish?
- ➢ How many times have you allowed the voice of your fear be louder than the voice of your heart?
- ➢ How do you want to feel when you wake up every single day of your life?

This is why you picked up this book. To go deep. To find your path. To March forward in your life in a way that feels truly, wholly, authentically YOU.

Each of us is here for a purpose in life. Our heart knows what that is, and how to get us there. When we understand all of the pieces that make up who we are, it becomes easier for us to quiet down enough to listen to our heart, and then make decisions and take the actions that DO feel right - so that we can get to the fun stuff in life – living our purpose, feeling happiness, joy, and a sense of freedom, no matter where we are on our journey, or what is happening in our lives.

It's not about having all the answers. It's not about being perfect by anyone else's standards. It's about embracing our own mess, asking ourselves some hard questions, and deciding how to use those answers to become who we really want to be.

Believe me when I say this...the possibilities really are endless!

So, get ready. In these pages, there is work to be done. This book is NOT going to give you a blueprint or set of rules for how to live your life, how to act, or what to believe. I am not going to tell you how to feel. Those are all your job to decide. What I am going to teach you is:

> Energy: what and where it is, how to use it, and why you should care
> Mindset: what it means, the types of mindsets, and how you can foster the mindset that works for you
> Tapping into your own, individual energy.
> Your Ego: what it is, why it is there, and how to quiet it down
> Intuition: what it is and how it speaks to you
> Self-love: what it is and why it's important
> Boundaries: what are they, why do we need them, and how to set and uphold them
> Setting goals that align with who you really are.

You are going to go on a journey, asking yourself some pretty tough questions along the way, so that you can start to understand what exactly you want in life, and how you want to feel every single day. Know that this process to understand yourself takes time, effort, and the desire to put your old stories aside. I believe that, by the sheer fact that you are here, you have already made that choice, and that is one decision for which you should be so proud of making.

You are 100% responsible for you; what you put into the world; what you think; how you feel; what you do. These are your responsibilities, and the only things that you can truly control in this lifetime. Once you figure that part out – that there really isn't anything that you can control except yourself – that gives you the canvas to script a new story, one that gives you back your power to be you. From there, the possibilities for your life are endless.

Are you ready? Let's get started!

And suddenly you just know it's time to start something new and trust the magic of beginnings.

Start Here, Begin Now!

You don't need any previous experience or knowledge to use this workbook. I only ask a few things...

> ➤ Grab a fresh, clean notebook and your favorite pen. For the most part, you will be able to do most of the exercises within the pages of this book. However, there might be some places where you want to write more, take a few notes, or explore a subject a little deeper. Get that notebook ready so that you have it when you need it.
>
> ➤ Set aside some time each day to work through the material. This is a marathon, not a sprint. There is no set timeframe for the book. You go at your own pace, according to your intuition and energy and schedule and goals. You might be called to go chapter-by-chapter all in the span of a few weeks, or you might decide to work through a chapter, let the material sit for a few days, and then come back to the book. That is okay, too. Allow the process to happen as it needs to for you!

As you move through each section:

> ➤ Make yourself comfortable, and sit in a space where you will not be disturbed.
> ➤ Dive in and give yourself permission to be honest with yourself.
> ➤ Tell yourself that you will stay open to learning, growth, and discovery.
> ➤ Bring an open mind and be ready to open your heart.
> ➤ And be honest with yourself! These are repeated, I know...they are that important!
> ➤ Be gentle with yourself. Don't judge what comes up. There are no rules or limits here, so don't hold yourself back out of fear that someone else will judge it either.

➢ Recognize that, by doing this work, you are opening yourself up to some discomfort. This is okay, and perfectly normal. Recognize it. But don't let it stop you.

Recognize that, at any given moment, you can take your power back from whatever situation has gotten the best of you, make a new choice and start over from a place of love and compassion. Your action plan starts by taking a snapshot of where you are now. Then, focus on the changes you want to make, and how you want to feel along the way.

Remember: You are 100% responsible for the results you create for your life! Take the time here to examine what you want, understand your mindset, know what is holding you back, and challenge that, so that you can let it go. Then, you can plan a strategy for moving forward, feeling excited and inspired, trusting that you will take the action steps needed.

Making the Commitment

Congratulations on your willingness to examine your situation from a new perspective. Congratulations on your commitment to yourself, and on making the choice to take your life into your own hands, making yourself accountable for your thoughts, feelings, decisions, actions, and outcomes.

Commitment is a powerful tool! It helps us focus and remain accountable for the choices we make. By making this choice, you are clearly saying:

- ✓ YES, to loving yourself!
- ✓ YES, to embracing a new life for yourself and for those around you!
- ✓ YES, to honoring each and every part of who you are!
- ✓ YES, to the impact you can have on the world!
- ✓ YES, to your future-self!
- ✓ YES, to possibilities!
- ✓ YES, to learning and growth and discovery!
- ✓ Yes, I AM ready for more!

Take a minute, right now, and commit to yourself and your progress. You might even consider printing this out and keeping it where you will see it often, as a way to keep yourself forward-focused.

➤ I, (state your name) _____, hereby commit to myself, that I am responsible for my own wellbeing. I commit to stepping outside of myself, taking steps to learn and grow, mentally, emotionally, physically, and spiritually.

➤ I commit that I will manage my own needs, and speak up when I need help.

➤ I commit to managing my own energy, and that I will make the effort to listen and trust the voice of my intuition.

➤ I commit to the willingness to do what it takes, to taking new actions, to trying new ideas, to stretching outside of my comfort zone.

➤ I commit that I am responsible for my success and happiness, and will hold myself accountable to uphold the standards I set for my life.

➤ I commit to being gentle and compassionate with myself as I step forward into what feels unfamiliar.

➤ I commit to celebrating my accomplishments.

➤ I am willing to stand for what is possible, and to avoid projection and judgement of myself and others.

➤ Finally, I commit to loving myself every step of the way.

Signed: _____   Date: _____

Intentions

An intention is a guiding thought for your actions. This is a powerful tool to manifest what you want for your life. Your intentions are energy, and help create your reality, giving you clarity on what you really want. When you take time to set an intention you focus on it. Then you act on it.

Intentions are not goals. Intentions are an attitude...a purpose...a direction. When you set out to do anything in life, no matter what you want to manifest, question your intentions.

Why do you want what you want? Why do you act the way you act? Is it for yourself? Is it for someone else? Are you acting out of the goodness of your heart, or because you are going to get something in return?

How do you form a true intention? First, connect with the energy of your heart. Sit for a few minutes and breathe. Then, think through some of these questions to help you form an intention.

- ➢ What matters most to you?
- ➢ What would you like to build, create, or nurture in your life?
- ➢ What would you like to let go of?
- ➢ Who would you like to forgive in your life?
- ➢ How do you feel when you are your happiest self?
- ➢ What makes you proud?
- ➢ What word(s) would you like to align yourself with?
- ➢ What fears would you like to release?
- ➢ What are you grateful for?
- ➢ How do you want to feel?

Here is your chance to form some intentions for this book.

What is it that brought you here? What do you hope to learn? Why did this book pop up for your now?

How would you like to see yourself at the end of this process? How will you know that growth has taken place? How would you feel?

Set 2 intentions for this book. What are the overall feelings you believe these intentions will be?

I intend....	I believe this intention will feel like...
1.	
2.	

You: A Snapshot in Time...

Far too often we think we need to wait to get started to do almost anything.

- ➤ Want to take that vacation?...Need to wait until next year.
- ➤ Want to get married?...Need to wait until I have enough money in the bank, a house, and my career set.
- ➤ Want to get myself a massage or a day to relax?...Need to wait until I get the laundry done, the house cleaned, and the bills paid.

These are excuses. Honestly, we are full of them.

When it comes to wanting to make changes in our lives, these excuses pop up all over the place. We say things like:

- ➤ I want to change my life...but I don't know how (so I won't do anything at all).
- ➤ I have tried that before, but it didn't work...so there must be something wrong with me - OR...so I can't do it anyway – OR there must be something wrong with the system I tried. So, I won't do anything at all.
- ➤ I didn't do that thing that I told my friend I would do ...she makes me so mad anyway sometimes, and isn't really my friend. So, I won't do anything at all.

Here's the kicker – it doesn't have to be that hard. We can kick the excuse-habit to the curb.

If you want to change your life – do something different, see different results, try something new, whatever it is – first, recognize that the excuses are going to be there. Then, take a deep breath and do it anyway. Those excuses are the voice of fear trying to keep you right where you are. It's a defense mechanism to keep you safe.

It doesn't have to be an all-or-nothing proposition, which is usually what we want. We want change to be fast and easy, without needing to take the time to do the work. Life isn't like that – sorry!

If you want change – real change that lasts – it needs to be done over time. Have patience! Rome wasn't built in a day, butterflies aren't just born, they evolve from a caterpillar, and your life – the one that is waiting for you and feels oh so good to be in – is going to take some time to emerge. We have to do a little bit of work to help the process along. This is okay. This is normal. You are okay.

Start from where we are right now. Today. In this moment. Take some time to honor, accept, and celebrate yourself and all that you have accomplished and overcome. Recognize that from this moment on, life is going to change. It's going to look different and feel different. You no longer want to feel stuck in your life anymore, and you are ready to take charge and live it your way.

Clarity: Who Are You and What Do You Want?

→ Do you know who you are? Really? Have you taken time to sit down and think about your personal identity, and what makes you really tick? What makes you come alive?

→ Do you know what you really want? Really? Have you taken time to sit down and think about what you want for your life, and what it would feel like to have it?

This is what we are going to do now. It's time to get some clarity on who you are and start to get clarity on what you want in life.

You start to form your identity from a pretty early age. As you move into your teen years, you start to question that identity. As you get a little more freedom and start to become more independent, you don't have a strong sense of who you are, and tend to feel lost. It makes it had to have a vision for what you really, truly, authentically want, but by the time we are somewhere around 18 years old, the world is telling us we need to know what we want for the future. How the heck are we supposed to know what is going to make us really, truly happy, when we don't even really truly know who the heck we are?

For many of us, by the time we get to our mid-twenties or early-thirties, we are sitting back and wondering "who am I?" and "is this all life has to offer?" By that point, though, too often, we are so stuck in the mindset that we have to have that traditional 9-5 job, or start a family, or stuck in a role that has been programmed and that we have practiced for so long.

But...

Transformation begins with awareness, and if we are going to start anything new, we need to have a baseline from which to work. This is how we gauge progress. We can look back over time and see changes taking place – in how we look, in how we feel, in how we spend our time, energy, and resources, even in the new goals we set for ourselves later down the road. While it is challenging to overcome fear and push through the resistance of setting new goals and creating new habits, looking at our journey up to this point, the good and the bad, gives us an appreciation for our lives. Life isn't all mess and doom and gloom. It is equally as important to call to mind people, places, and things that are important and positive, as it is to look at what is not working, so that we can move forward with a sense of optimism, instead of a mentality of lack or self-loathing. These make it difficult to move forward.

Take a few minutes to think about who you are right now. Grab your journal, in case you need some extra space.

Whom did you wake up as this morning? Describe yourself physically, emotionally, mentally, physically, and spiritually. What does life feel like for you right now?

Describe the "mess" that you find yourself in right now. What has life presented you? How does this situation continue to pop up in your life? Why?

What are you trying to avoid by ignoring this mess?

What is working well in your life right now? Think about areas of love/relationships/family, money, career, health and physical body, living your purpose, spirituality, personal growth.

What needs to change to improve your situation? How would you like to see the above areas become even better?

What are your biggest frustrations?

What are your hobbies?

What are your favorite foods?

What type of music do you like?

_____

What is your favorite color?

_____

What do you think or dream about most often?

_____

What are your strengths? Natural gifts? Skills? Talents?

_____

What do you fear the most?

When have you felt truly alive?

What do you love to do? What did you love to do as a kid?

What are your perceived weaknesses?

What types of activities are you interested in trying?

Where do you feel safest?

When you are sad or upset, how are you most comforted? What makes you feel supported?

What subjects or topics matter to you most?

When you look back over your life, list your top 5 or 10 proudest accomplishments.

For whom, or what, are you most grateful?

What are your top 3 memories?

What would you do if you knew failure wasn't an option and you would achieve your goal, guaranteed? Would that change your level of commitment? Why or why not?

What are you passionate about?

Activity: Current Self v. Future Self: A Visual

In the box on the left, draw a picture to represent your current self. What does he/she look like? Feel like? Then, in the box on the right, think about how you want to look and feel in the future and do the same thing. What do you look like? How does life feel? What is different about who you are?

If you don't feel like you can adequately represent these with a drawing, you can also do this with photos from magazines. Find representations of you now, and then those that represent you in the future.

Current Self	Future Self

What 3 words would you use to describe the best version of you NOW?

     1. _____

     2. _____

     3. _____

What 3 words would you use to describe the best version of the person you want to become?

     1. _____

     2. _____

     3. _____

Authenticity

What the heck is an "authentic self"?

Your authentic self is the you that is you when all the masks come off, when everyone else's opinions and judgements and ideas fall away, and you are able to express yourself fully, and completely, as YOU choose, in a way that feels good for you.

Living authentically means that you can listen to the opinions of other people, without worrying if you need to change your mind to match theirs. You don't feel the need to push your opinions onto other people either.

An authentic life is one in which you flow, day-to-day, moment-by-moment, in touch with your energy and intuition, and easily able to adapt and redirect when you need to.

Without integrity, there can be no purpose. All progress stops!

This can be scary at times, because it involves listening to our intuition, and trusting that the guidance is right, even when it makes no sense at all, and even when we don't see the connection between the guidance and our calling.

You know what you want. You cannot make true progress towards living with a sense of freedom and peace, until you are living in alignment, with integrity, honoring who you are at the core of your being.

An inspired life is one where you are in alignment with your purpose, your goals, values, beliefs. You wake up every single day excited, trusting yourself, that you are using your mind in service of your heart. You are living with integrity, because you are doing the things that align with your authentic self.

What are you afraid of?

A few words on fear and failure...

We can't talk about creating change in our lives without talking about fear. No matter how hard we try to avoid or resist it, it's there, inside every single one of us. There is no getting around it, or avoiding it. The challenge comes because our fear isn't always so obvious, and it presents itself in so many different ways. It doesn't go away – ever. With every new choice and action, fear comes back looking slightly different than the last time we recognized it.

Our goal becomes this: feel the fear, then do things anyway. We avoid taking action, usually because we are telling ourselves something like this: "I'll do it when I am not afraid anymore." We tell ourselves that we can't/shouldn't/won't do something, and convince ourselves that this story is true, because of fear.

Fear is a liar. It doesn't speak to you with logic, or facts. It uses illusion to scare you, and speaks with a voice that says "hell, no! No way! I can't do this!"

Fear comes in all forms. Anxiety. Depression. Anger. Exhaustion. Denial. Distraction.

It talks to us this way, to keep us safe, to help us avoid failure. The dreaded "F" word when you are trying to transform your life. Our ego has us believe that, when we fail at something, we weren't successful. We didn't achieve our goals.

Here's the problem...success and failure are subjective. Far too often, we don't take time to define what those mean for ourselves, so we let the world around us dictate what they should mean. Then, we spend our precious time, energy, and resources trying to keep up with that, instead of what we really want.

Have you ever felt paralyzed with fear? It doesn't feel so good, does it? When it comes to trying something new in our life, usually, that fear comes because we don't want to be judged. We get so concerned that someone else is going to say we are bad or wrong or stupid for even trying, and that judgement, which might or might not even happen, becomes the thing that keeps us paralyzed. Here's a question for you...

Why is everyone else's opinion more important or valid or valuable than your own?

Don't get me wrong. Fear can be a good thing. It comes from the ego, which is the voice inside of each of us telling us to avoid situations that will bring us pain, or, worse, kill us. It's here to remind you to:

- ✓ Use an oven mitt when getting something out of the oven.
- ✓ Look both ways before you cross the street.
- ✓ Run as fast as possible when the tiger is coming at you, or kill it so that our caveman family will eat this winter.

It's a fight-or-flight response programming us for survival. Whenever you want to make a change, your ego is going to convince you that, by doing so, you will die. It's extreme to think about, but that is how our brains are programmed. The problem is: we aren't living in the caveman days anymore, yet fear continues to cause us to fight or flee.

It's important to be aware of this, as well as the story you continue to tell yourself. Then, you can question whether the story is based on fact, or fiction. Is your story based on truths, or what you perceive as other people doing to you?

> - ➤ Did someone else make you feel bad?
> - ➤ Did someone else make you angry?
> - ➤ Was someone else angry at you?
> - ➤ Do you tell yourself it wasn't your fault...no matter the reason why?

- ➤ Have you ever said something like "I can't do it because someone else did _____ to me, and now I feel ___?"
- ➤ Excuses! Excuses! Excuses!

In reality, nobody made you do anything, or feel any particular way. You chose it. We aren't taught this as kids. We are raised to believe that, because someone yelled at us, we are bad or did something wrong. We are programmed to make those connections that put other people in charge of our feelings. Any time you want to do something new, fear sets in, and those connections start to appear all over again.

This can change. Once you recognize patterns in your life – in your thoughts, feelings, and actions – you can recognize the fear. It is then your personal responsibility to take action, quieting down the fear and moving forward in your life anyway.

Nobody made you feel fear. That was a perception that you adopted based on the world around you, sometimes based on someone else's actions. Those actions were based on someone else's story – their perception of how the world works. It was never about you in the first place. Why hold onto that and let the fear keep you in hiding? How is that fair to you?

It's not! So, stop holding onto that perception. Stop making it part of your identity.

The fear is always going to be there. Acknowledge that. On the path of personal development, fear continues to rear its ugly head, trying to push you away from what you want. No matter how many times you evolve and grow, there will be themes that continue to pop up, causes you to resist taking action. It's your job to understand when it's fear talking versus your intuition. We will get into intuition later on in the book. For now, understand that fear never truly goes away. Understand this. Be aware of your thoughts, feelings, and actions, so that when it comes screaming, you know what to do to stay on track. Remember that your excuses are the voice of fear.

The truth is: you are a boundless, limitless ball of energy. Remember this the next time fear tries to tell you to stop.

— FEAR —

**"Too many of us are not
living our dreams because
we are living our fears."**
- Les Brown

What are you afraid of? What do you worry about most often?

Why?

What is the likelihood that the fear is real? Is it based on your own perception or someone else's?

What defines "failure" for you? Why?

What would you tell a friend who failed at something they really wanted to succeed at?

Has there ever been a time when you saw the benefit of a failure?

What has been the best mistake you ever made?

Have you ever lied about a failure? What was the situation? Why did you feel you needed to lie about it?

Understanding Energy

There are a lot of personal transformation out there that refers to energy, and specifically relates it to the energy of the physical world – how much energy we need to go about our daily tasks each day; the energy that, when depleted, often has us running to the nearby coffee shop for a caffeine kick. This is part of it, but energy is so much more than this.

What is energy? How does it affect you and your life? How does it impact intuition? I answer those questions with a few questions right back at you:

→ Have you ever felt totally stuck, and unsure how to move forward?

→ Have you ever felt exhausted or anxious for seemingly no reason at the thought of certain tasks, activities, or spending time with certain people?

→ Have you ever felt like you needed to do something, but didn't trust that it made any sense at all, so you didn't follow through?

→ Did you ever find yourself in a crowded place and suddenly you feel anxious or tired or angry and didn't know why?

→ Have you ever met someone who seems okay on the surface, but deep down you felt like there was something missing, or "off"?

If you find yourself answering "yes" to the above, you already are aware of the energy around you. We all have a physical body and an energetic body. Our energy is transmitting and recording thoughts and interactions with the physical world around you, and evaluates each interaction and experience and person that crosses our path.

Everything is made of energy, and everyone. All energy exists in one of the following ways, vibrating at different frequencies, each one faster than the one before:

→ 3D-physical world

→ Our ego, thoughts, emotions

→ Our consciousness, outside of our body and thoughts, our aura

Emotions such as love and gratitude are very high-vibrational emotions, and feelings like sadness and hate are very low-vibe. The high-vibrational emotions are magnetic; they attract things to us. On the flip side, when your vibration is high, you might feel happy, calm, and peaceful. The right people arrive at the right time and place, and things are flowing with ease. Your "vibe" is a combination, the sum, of the frequencies of each of these. This is why you can feel like you have a ton of energy, but feel emotionally distant. One is at a higher vibration.

Energy is a valuable resource. One's individual energy is not the same as anyone else's. We are all unique. What one person has the capacity for differs from the person working at the cubicle next door. That's not to say that some people naturally will go farther and accomplish more in life. That couldn't be further from the truth! Everyone has the potential (energy) to excel, the potential (energy) for greatness, and the potential (energy) to achieve anything and everything they want in their lifetime.

The key is to know when and how to use that energy.

Just like your energy vibrates at a specific frequency, so does the energy of other people, places and things. This is why you "vibe" with some people and not others. This is also why certain places might feel "off" to you when you walk in. The energy doesn't match wherever you are energetically. It doesn't feel right. It's not an energetic match. When two things or two people are an energetic match, it feels good. It feels right. It is easy to enjoy it. There is no resistance to or for it.

We are born into this lifetime feeling our way through the world. As babies, we are great readers of energy. We know who and what is "safe" and what is not. This is where our energetic programming begins. Many of our subconscious thoughts are programmed into us between the ages of 0 and 8 years old, when we are like tiny, human sponges, soaking in every situation, every feeling, that crosses our path. Information from these experiences is stored. That "information" is energy, and we use it to help us navigate through life.

Our minds are using this information from the perspective of that initial experience. So, if you have a negative experience at the age of 5 that causes you to hold onto the feeling of unworthiness, as an adult, any time a situation that comes up that triggers that feeling of unworthiness is brought up from the perspective of your five-year-old self. Your brain cannot tell the difference between something that happened in the past and something that is happening right now. Logically, the current situation might not be one that warrants such a triggered, heightened state, but your brain does not know the difference.

Our minds are constantly going, even when we do not realize it. We think somewhere between 50,000 and 70,000 thoughts per day. Since our brain is wired to focus on the negative as a mechanism to keep us safe, most of our thoughts are actually negative. Why is this important? Because those subconscious thoughts – the ones happening in the background that you do not even realize – are also sending information out to the Universe. These thoughts play a part in how you show up in the world, the decisions you make, the action you take, and what is manifest in your life.

How we connect with, understand, and use this energy matters! And what many don't realize is: energetic blocks can form when we don't manage our energy appropriately. If we push and resist when the Universe is telling us to rest, we end up depleted of our own, individual resources, and a block is formed. When the world is telling us to go-go-go, often we start to listen to that more than our intuitive energy. Our Ego energy wants us to believe that, because those "go-go-go" messages hit us en masse (i.e. it's the way society wants us to work), they must be true.

This...Is...Bullshit!

Just like in science class, while energy cannot be created or destroyed, it can be depleted. Work too fast, or exert more power than needed, energy and resources are used quickly, and we might not be able to get the work done on time. This is why intuition is important. Listening to our bodies. Taking time to think before we dive head first.

Blocks can continue to build in our energy field, slowing or stopping the flow of energy. Think of it like an energetic dam that continues to build. Over time, that dam gets bigger and bigger, as we take in and hold onto more energy - more "stuff" that belongs to other people or situations. Eventually, that dam is going to burst.

We hold onto the energy of the situation, the energy of our thoughts, the energy of other people involved in our lives, taking it all with us through our lifetime. If everything is running smooth, energy is flowing freely, and you have a much easier time manifesting what you want. On the other hand, if things are always negative, if we are always around negative people, places, situations, store the energy and emotions of these experiences. Eventually, blocks are created in our energetic system. This holds us back from where we want to be.

If you continue to rehash old emotions in your system, old beliefs, the blockages continue to build. You end up living in a constant state of stress. Your body doesn't like this. Over time, your body becomes conditioned to live in a never-ending state of negativity, so much so that your body starts to think this is normal. Our problems, our "mess," continue to trigger the feelings of sadness, hopelessness, and that we are stuck in our own lives. It leaves us narrowly focused on the environment around you, and how much time you have to get stuff done. We can't create. We can't open our heart. We can't sit still long enough to think through problems that arise. This throws us into a mentality if lack and gives us to propensity to control as much as possible around us.

It's important to understand this: Energy is everywhere. You cannot run or hide from it, no matter how hard you try. How you feel physically is a direct correlation to your energy, to what you are holding onto energetically, and to the energy of those around you. In addition, how you feel about things like money, time, and relationships, all relate to the energy of experiences from earlier in our lifetime.

And...if energy that stays blocked over time can cause us to stay in more of a negative mindset, removing those blockages can likewise give us more of a sense of peace, love, and joy in our lives. In this state, it becomes much easier to handle stress and easier to move through any situation that presents itself to us.

Being aware of the energy within and around you is not some secret party trick, reserved for those who are deemed "fit" or "worthy." Actually, it is something we are all capable of tapping into. We are all born with the ability. As kids, it's easier for us to access it. This is why babies cry instantly when some people come into their presence, but smile for others. They learn what is safe in the world through the energy that is around them.

Why care about energy – ours or anyone else's? I have asked this often myself.

Because we, as individuals, are way more, way bigger, than our physical bodies could ever be! There are limitless possibilities around you, and you can create the life that you truly want.

Remember that everything is energy. You can't create or destroy it, but you can transfer it. This means that you can change the cycle. You can remove the blockages, open the dam, and get energy flowing through you again. You are not powerless or stuck in any situation.

When you are open and receptive to the energy around you, you can approach conversations and situations from a new point of view. It becomes easier to feel into things and perceive whether or not the situation is "safe" or "right" or "true" for us. Instead of spending time and energy trying to sort through logic to determine if someone is telling us the truth, we can intuitively feel our way through any situation, and know whether or not something is an energetic match for us or not. And it becomes easier, faster, and way more fun, to manifest what we want in our lives. Taking the attention off the people, places, things, and situations, get your attention off of time and matter, out of the 3D, you can break the cycle. You open your awareness to energy instead.

In addition, understanding the energy around you can also give you a window into someone else's experiences and feelings, allowing you to feel into their point of view. In times when there is conflict or disagreement, instead of meeting resistance with resistance, you can redirect the conversation so that it can be more productive, asking new questions that are a better match for both parties. When you feel into a situation and know that someone else isn't feeling great, you can show up in a new way – one that is more supportive, showing genuine concern for where the other person is in that moment.

Let's face it – we live in a busy world. Far too often, life is more go-go-go than anything else, and this makes it really tricky to perceive the world around you on an energetic level – this includes our own, individual energy. While we are boundless and limitless in potential, our physical bodies have a finite amount of energy. Because of this, it's so important to be able to feel into our energy, so that we can allocate our time and resources appropriately. Then, we can get the things done that really matter to us.

Slowing down and having mindful awareness, without distractions, is key. Put your phone or computer away when talking with other people in person. If you are talking via chat, close other apps. Stop multitasking when you are able to, and start listening, energetically listening, to the world around you. You will be amazed at how much more you can get done, how much better you feel, and how much better relationships can get. Watch for the evidence that life is getting more fun, exciting, and enjoyable, and recognize that the narrative you are playing in your mind is changing.

Where do you currently put your time and attention? Think – people, places and things. Are you using your energy wisely?

Now, ask yourself: If I am placing my attention here, is it for my highest good? Does this help or hinder progress?

What does the word "sabotage" mean to you? Do you find yourself sabotaging away your goals and dreams? How? When you think about this, how does it feel?

What 4 words or phrases would you use to describe the energy you would like to project in the world?

List a few things - people, places, things, phrases - that bring you a feeling of joy. Where in your body do you feel the joy? Describe the joy.

List a few things - people, places, things, phrases - that bring you a feeling of sadness, anger, or pain. Where in your body do you feel this? Describe it.

Look back at questions 5 and 6 above. Did you notice a shift in your overall feeling, your overall energy, when you brought these forward? Describe the shift.

A Meditation: Feeling Into Your Energy

Take time to sit in stillness and quiet, and allow yourself to be fully present, without distraction from the outside world. Feel free to put some soft music on while you complete this meditation. For the first part of this exercise, take time to simply notice the sensations in and around you. Don't try to change anything, and don't judge it. Allow it to be whatever it is in the moment.

> ➤ First, take a minute and think about how you feel right now. What is your overall mood? How does your body feel?
> ➤ Set a timer for 5 minutes.
> ➤ Take a few deep breaths, inhaling through your nose to a count of 4, and exhaling through your nose to a count of 4.
> ➤ Become aware of the sensations in your body. Notice if you feel any tension or tightness. Where do you feel it most?
> ➤ Do you feel tired or anxious?
> ➤ Stay present in the moment. If you notice your thoughts start to wander, bring it back to here and now, and the feeling of your energy in and around your body.
> ➤ When the timer goes off, gently wiggle your fingers and toes, and when you are ready, open your eyes.
> ➤ How do you feel? Has anything changed since you started this activity?

We are all like energetic sponges, reading the energy around us at all times. This makes it easy for us to get overwhelmed and bogged down, as we take in this information. It's like sensory overload for our energetic bodies. Sometimes, even the simplest of things, like taking a deep breath, helps to clear away any energetic crud, allowing us to feel our own energy and listen to our own thoughts.

Take a few minutes to repeat the above activity. This time, make sure you have a pen to answer the questions below along the way.

Become aware of your thoughts. What do you think about when you first wake up? Are there thoughts coming up for you, right now, that appear throughout the day? Is your thinking fixed or flexible? Where do you feel it in your body?

Close your eyes. Where do you feel tightness or tension in your body? Are you breathing freely? Are you relaxed? Do you feel tired or energetic?

Right now, wiggle your fingers and toes. Move your body. What happens when you move your arms? How about your legs? Are there certain thoughts or feelings that come up? How does this make you feel? Do you feel like you want to restrict yourself from movement, or can you move freely?

Make some noise. Say "yes" and "no" - is one easier to say than the other? Which one? How do they feel?

Sing and make noise. Can you do so without judging yourself? How does it feel?

Ask: Where are you forcing life to happen? Are you being too demanding on yourself or others?

How do you feel when you are around certain people, or in particular places? Describe those feelings.

Make note of your breath and your body. Do you expand or contract?

Make a list of different feelings - happy, sad, scared, angry, etc. What are your beliefs or images about those feelings? Where do you tend to feel those feelings, if at all, in your body?

Do you consider yourself to be a thinker, feeler, or doer? Why? When did you first begin to identify yourself as such? Does that feel "right" to you?

Think about someone you live or work with. Observe and feel their energy. How do you feel in their presence? Are you invited in or kept at bay? Do you feel they hold back, hold in, hold up, collapse, or scatter their energy?

Energetic Blocks and Letting Go

Remember – we take in experiences from the outside world, and hold onto the energy of those experiences throughout our lifetime. If we don't resolve any conflicts that arise from these experiences, either with other people or within ourselves, energetic blocks form. These blocks can show up in a variety of ways, mentally, emotionally, physically, and spiritually, and these blocks impact more than our energy; they also correlate to the story we tell ourselves time and time again.

Below are some common signs of energetic blocks. Have you ever felt any of these? Circle the ones that feel familiar to you.

Need to control others Controlling the environment Lack of motivation Lack of direction Feeling helpless Shame Needing to be secretive Feeling like a victim Lots of ideas – no action Choosing to isolate Lack of compassion for self Lack of compassion for others	Inability to see the big picture Inability to see beauty of life Inability to speak your mind Inability to accept opinions Judging others Intense guilt Frequent or intense anger Getting lost in your thoughts Feeling numb Dominating conversations Feeling overly stimulated	Lack of responsibility for self Using words to hurt others Using words to hurt yourself Extreme fatigue or exhaustion Stomach aches Headaches Anxiety or restlessness Nervousness Tension Mood swings

It can be a challenge to understand our energetic blocks. They can be difficult to spot. Our mind stops us from acknowledging them, because, often it involves looking at painful events from our past. It can feel scary, uncomfortable, and maybe bring up frustration, anger, or sadness that we completely forgot about, or didn't even realize, we held onto. It doesn't feel good in the moment. Ultimately, it's totally worth it.

So, how do you let go? You gotta' feel it to heal it!

We store emotions in our bodies. Holding onto things that make us feel sad, stuck, lost, or angry leaves less, or no, room for things that make us feel good. Once you allow yourself to feel into the situation, feel that emotion, you can release the energy and let it go. This frees up energetic space for you to fill with something new, different, better for your life. It allows you to redirect your thoughts and emotions, and see situations that previously caused pain from a new perspective. Here is where a new story can start to emerge. If you have identified areas where your energy is blocked or effected, it's time to remove the blocks and free that energy up so that you can create whatever it is that will bring you joy and happiness. This is how do you raise your vibration. Ultimately, this is how you continue to "level up" and attract new and better people, situations, or things to your life.

Are you ready to release these emotions, let them go and fill the space with something else entirely? Some ways to accomplish this release include:

- Cry.
- Recall the situation and dance it out of yourself.
- Write a letter to yourself in that situation and tell yourself that it's okay to feel the way you feel, and that everything is going to be okay.
- Write a letter to someone who hurt you in the past. You can send the letter, or rip it up and bury it in the ground. Ask the Universe to take that energy and return it to happier, higher vibrational energy.
- Remember why you are looking to make changes in your life. Spend time focusing on YOU. Self-care is so important! What makes you feel fabulous? DO IT. Schedule that time for yourself on a regular basis.
- Become conscious of your thoughts. Over time, the more aware of them you become, the easier it gets to change them. More on this later.
- Be aware of how you talk to yourself.
- Notice what foods you eat, and make it a point to make sure you are getting the proper balance of nutrients in your diet. Foods like broccoli and blueberries are higher-vibrational foods. Foods that are produced with chemical additives are lower-vibrational foods. Become mindful of how your body feels as you eat different foods. You do not have to make huge changes all at once, just become aware of your body and how it feels.
- Drink plenty of water.
- Exercise. Get out into the sun and spend time in nature.
- Practice acts of kindness. Do something nice for someone else.
- Spend time with the people that you love, and who makes you feel loved, nurtured, supported, and inspired.
- Sing! Speak! Express yourself.
- Seek help from an energy healer, like a shaman or reiki practitioner.

As you look back at the blocks you circled above, from where do you believe they originated?

When you think about these, which are the ones that pop up more frequently? Look back at events in your life and try to connect the emotions with these experiences. What comes up?

Think back to yesterday. Then, think back to last week. What emotions do you remember (be honest)? At what or to whom were they directed? Where did they come from?

Do you notice any patterns? What stories do you repeat to yourself in relation to these emotions or thoughts?

How often do I keep my promises to myself or others?

What unfinished business or project might be creating obstacles in your life?

Do you have a personal code of honor? What is it?

Do you often find yourself exaggerating or embellishing facts to support your point of view or your personal story? Why? How does this make you feel?

Are you critical of others? Do you blame others as a way to protect yourself?

Do you seek out approval from other people? Why?

Are there any relationships in your life that require healing? Which ones?

Mindset

When we talk about mindset, we are referring to our attitudes and beliefs, and whether we perceive the world as positive or negative. Your mindset influences how you act, think, feel, and what you do. It can be fixed or set for growth.

Into which category do you think you fall?

With a fixed mindset, you believe that you are the way you are, and you think how you think, and that none of it can or will ever change. You are set in your ways and believe that talent alone is required for success, without the need for effort. You believe that you came into the world with all of the intelligence you will ever have. With a fixed mindset, setbacks are discouraging, because they make you believe you are incapable of accomplishing a goal or a task. If you seek change, or try to implement a new system for your life, you are likely to quit pretty early in the process. It's a very defeating mentality.

When the fixed mindset starts to speak, it says things like: "you can't do ___", or "past mistakes are failures," or "you can never do better for yourself." In those moments, give it a quick shhhhh! And remind yourself that you can! Then, go find someone who can help you see it from a new perspective. Look for a tool or resource that you can use to learn. There are so many strategies out there. Find what works for you.

With a growth mindset, you believe that your learning and intelligence can change over time. Experience shapes your beliefs. You believe that you CAN become smarter, and are willing to put in the effort because it impacts overall success. Setbacks are viewed as learning opportunities, not failures. Because of this, when you seek out change, you are in it for the long game. You know there are going to be obstacles thrown in your path, and you welcome them as opportunities, not setbacks.

You want to continue learning, refining your skills, and you are open to listening to the thoughts and opinions of others, because you see them, too, as teachers. This sets you up for growth and development, and can propel you forward.

In reality, there are other types of mindset, and the good news is this: your mindset can change. Just like you can change your energy, just like you can change how you feel about a situation, and just like how you can change your thoughts, beliefs, and opinions, your mindset is not fixed. This takes awareness and commitment and the choice to see things a new way! Once you have the awareness, give yourself permission to try again. You are never stuck!

Understanding and upgrading your mindset involves knowing yourself and what triggers you. Think back to some of the energetic blocks.

> - Are you stressed? Angry? Bored?
> - Is there trauma that needs to be addressed?
> - Have you taken care of yourself – gotten enough sleep/water/proper foods?
> - Did someone say something to you that reminded you of a painful situation from the past?

Knowing your triggers puts you in control, so that you can plan for what to do to help yourself get out of an uncomfortable situation. It becomes easier to adopt a new story for your life, when you are able to recognize the triggers – it keeps you out of the victim mindset, which keeps you paralyzed and stuck. First, recognize that the trigger is there to teach you; it's an opportunity to grow. It is uncomfortable, yes. It is temporary, and won't last forever. Prepare for them. Understand how your energy is impacted when the triggers come up, and have awareness for your body, so that you can tell when your energy shifts. You might notice:

- ➢ You are anxious.
- ➢ You are tired.
- ➢ You feel anger.
- ➢ Your body tenses up, maybe your jaw is tight.
- ➢ You have headaches.
- ➢ You talk faster than normal.
- ➢ ...Remember: these are not the same for everyone!

Changing your mindset takes commitment. It is a process. Have people in your corner who support you, and who share in the mindset you are choosing for yourself.

Having the right mindset is important for success, no matter what you are trying to accomplish. Think of it like a muscle that needs constant toning and conditioning. The more you are aware of your mindset, the easier it becomes to tune in with what's going on – how you talk to yourself on a regular basis, how your body feels -- so you can work on getting rid of the type of self-talk that prevents you from focusing on the things you want to achieve. The goal is to focus more on the feelings, thoughts and actions that feel good, and are going to propel you forward.

Sometimes, life happens, and that is when our mindset tends to get the best of us. We start to move into negativity, blame, and shame. We don't need to keep ourselves down in the dumps, thought. We have the power to decide when and how we think and feel. Our mindset impacts the story we tell ourselves, which impacts our actions.

Remember – your life is your responsibility. How you think, feel, act, how you show up in the world, and what you believe are all entirely up to you.

Types of Mindset

Fixed and growth mindset are two examples of how we can look at the world and our lives. There are others. It is important to remember that mindset does not have to be fixed. By committing to a growth mindset, you open yourself up to so many more experiences and opportunities in your life.

Remember, too, that, each mindset has both positive and negative qualities. No single mindset is better, or the only right way to think. And, just like our energy changes, our mindset likely also shifts depending on our energy, or the experiences around us.

Social Mindset:	Fear Mindset:
You like hanging out with other people and are open to new cultures and new ways of life. It is easy to make friends, and you tend to communicate well. This can lead to a tendency to be overly concerned with how others see you.	A little fear is important to keep us safe. With a fear-based mindset, you are unable to allow yourself to have new experiences or go on adventures. The fear leaves you living in a shell and it could be difficult to find your purpose.
Abundance Mindset:	**Scarcity Mindset:**
You believe there is plenty for everyone. We all have equal access to wealth, happiness, love, prestige, and success. You tend to focus on the overall big picture. Because you feel that there is enough for everyone, perhaps you do not aim as high as you could because everyone wins.	There is never enough of anything – food, money, love, time, resources. This leads to feeling as though your needs are not and might never be met. It might also cause you to work harder to success.

Creativity Mindset: Creativity extends beyond art class. With a creative mindset, you can create new and unique ideas and are great at solving problems.	**Gratitude Mindset:** You are thankful for everything you have in life, and you are appreciating the people, places, and situations that arise for you.
Confidence Mindset: Confidence impacts how we think about ourselves and our abilities. With a confident mindset, it is a little easier to take risks. Over-confidence, however, can seem like arrogance.	**Envy Mindset:** You look at how others are doing in terms of money, relationships, etc. You likely keep score, and maybe feel a little jealous.
Dreamer Mindset: You think a lot, and you think big. You believe anything is possible and you can easily see a vision for your life.	**Giving Mindset:** You inspired by service to others. You live to give. You know how to use your gifts, talents, skills to help others.

What is something that you want to learn? What can you teach? What skills and talents do you have? Do you believe these can change? What do my thoughts tell me about how successful I can or will be at learning or teaching these things?

Do I set and maintain high standards for myself? Why or why not?

When in your life have you ever believed that you couldn't make the change you desired? Write about that here, as well as any thought patterns you remember from that time. How did you talk to yourself? Did you do anything specific to get yourself out of that mindset?

Which mindset do you most associate with? How has it helped and/or hindered you up until this point?

Why is this mindset no longer helping you get where you want to be? What thought patterns do you have regularly that stem from this mindset?

What mindset would you like to have? What thoughts would you like to think more often?

Do you take risks often? If yes, why? If not, why not? How do you talk to yourself when it comes to risk? What would I want a mentor to say to me when she/he sees me taking a risk or trying hard to push past obstacles?

What has helped you to move past doubt or fear? How do you talk to yourself or others when you feel fear? How has that helped, or hindered, you? What mindset(s) do these relate to?

What thoughts, words, or phrases pop into your head most often?

What are some new thought patterns you can tell yourself to start to retrain your mind?

What are some new actions you can take to further support these thoughts?

Limiting Beliefs

Why you have stopped yourself from taking these steps forward? What is holding you back?

Our beliefs are the lens through which we view the world, and determine if we define something as good or bad, true or false, possible or impossible. Belief defines our actions. Think of them like the unspoken rules we hold for ourselves, whether they are in our highest good or not. They are the words or phrases that we hold true, and define how we think, act, and say.

Beliefs are either limiting or empowering. Empowering beliefs are positive and propel us forward; things like "I am capable of achieving my goals" or "I am worthy of success." Limiting beliefs are those negative things we believe and include things like "I can't achieve my goals," or "I must have a certain amount of money before someone will love me."

Just like we can change our mindset, and just like we can impact our energy, we can change our beliefs! Doing this requires the awareness of the limiting beliefs, as well as their origin and all the ways they have benefited us in our lives. Then, we can start to re-frame these beliefs into more positive statements that we adopt over time.

Hang on, Liz...I thought you said limiting beliefs held us back. How could we have benefited? Great question! I am so glad you asked.

When you start to get honest with yourself, and challenge those limiting beliefs, you start to see patterns in your life. As an example, if you ever struggled with weight, perhaps you held the belief that the weight signified that there was something wrong with you, that people did not love you because of the weight. Instead of focusing on your health goals for yourself, it became an extrinsic motivation, with the emphasis on the love from others coming as a result. I.E.: the belief that losing the weight would bring love. Even though it is not necessarily positive, there was something to be gained by holding onto the belief that, by losing this weight, love would appear.

As you challenge this, you might come to see that holding onto the weight benefited you, by giving you a body in which you could hide yourself from the world. Maybe there was trauma, bullying, teasing, that made you feel unlovable. Holding onto the weight offered protection from the world and gives the feeling of safety.

Beliefs form from an incredibly young age, at a time when our logical thinking has not completely formed. Basically, stuff happened to us that we couldn't necessarily control. We assigned a meaning, or belief, to these situations, seeing it through a particular lens. Understand that these formed at a time when you did not have enough information to make an educated decision. Because of this, you might start to see that some of them don't really make sense. This is okay...now you do! And now, it's time to can change these beliefs into something more beneficial in your life.

You can't always control what happens in your life. But you can always control your thoughts and actions and emotions in response to a situation. When you know and feel this, fact, you become unstoppable! It doesn't matter what happens around you, because, ultimately, you are riding the roller coaster of life, resistance-free, hands up, enjoying the ride.

What are my excuses for why I don't have what I want? When was the first time I heard this? How many times has it impacted my life since?

From whom would you turn away when you find success? To whom would you owe an explanation for your success? Will they want to take your success away? Does this cause you to play it safe in life?

What will you lose when you get what you want?

What messages did you learn about money? From where or whom?

How did you learn about self-care? What messages did you learn?

Family Beliefs:

What were some of the ideas that you heard family members say to, or about you?

What values did they try to instill?

Who were some of those family members with whom you were closest? What messages did you learn from them?

Education:

Who were some of your most-influential teachers?

_____
What were some of the things you learned from them?

How much importance did you place on their message?

_____

What values did you learn through education?

_____

Experience:
_____
What experiences have you had that shape how you think?

Where or how did you learn about love? What was the message?

What messages did you learn about money?

Are the values you learned mostly positive or negative?

Do they limit or hold you back, or inspire you?

What would be different if you let the limiting messages go? How would you feel? What would you think? How would you act?

It's important to acknowledge when it's time to let go of old thought patterns. It's one thing to recognize that you have these thoughts. It's an entirely different situation to acknowledge that they aren't working for you anymore. Sometimes, we need to give ourselves permission to move forward.

Are you willing to let go of your limiting beliefs? If not, why not? If yes, why now?

How would things be different if you focused more on the empowering beliefs? Would you be willing to take more risks? Speak up more? Believe in yourself more?

What are you holding onto that you need to let go of? Can you see how it's holding you back? Why is this no longer working for you? How is it keeping you from the life you want?

What will it cost you if you do not release limiting beliefs?

Describe who you are without the limiting beliefs.

Flipping the Script and Resetting the Mind

Let's be honest: The old ways are not working. If they were, you wouldn't be here right now. What got you to this point is not going to get you to where you want to go. This is exciting to acknowledge! Now, here's the thing: you need to rewire this new script into your brain, which takes time and conscious effort. Consistency is key here. Remind yourself of the new beliefs you want to anchor in. Over time, you will notice changes in how you think, because these new beliefs are becoming part of your identity. You will notice changes in your actions, because they will be aligned with how you think. You will notice that the old ways of thinking don't feel right anymore. This is a slow and gradual process, but, as it evolves, and as you continue to grow, it feels pretty amazing. Over time, you will see a new version of yourself emerge. Those limiting beliefs are heavy, dense balls of low-vibrational energy, which keep you stuck, dead in your tracks. You deserve better than that!

Remember:

→ Recognize the repeating patterns of your thoughts.
→ Don't just accept circumstances as they are. You have the power to change them!
→ Reframe challenges and fears. Understand that they are calling you to do better, think better, and be better!
→ On the other side of your fear is your freedom!

As you start to examine and update your mindset, and let go of limiting beliefs, anchoring in some new daily practices will be helpful. Try to incorporate a few, or all of these in the next few days and weeks. Notice how you feel.

→ Connect with likeminded people.
→ Remove toxicity from your days.
→ Move your body.
→ Schedule time to relax.

→ Say no!

→ Schedule "tech-free time" each day.

→ Increase water intake.

→ Get a massage.

→ Eat healthy foods. Take a cooking class. Talk with a nutritionist if you need help updating your diet.

→ Laugh.

→ Read.

→ Hire and work with a coach.

→ Journal.

New Morning Practices

There is a saying: "win the morning, win the day." If you are able to get your day started, and avoid the distractions and energetic crud from the outside world, you give yourself the opportunity the sit with yourself, feel your own energy, tap into your intuition, read, and do other things that make you feel stronger, happier, and more confident in your life. Try this in the morning:

→ 3-5 minutes of deep breathing/meditation.

→ Free write and journal about anything that is worrying you, or that you fear. Don't overthink this or try to edit it. Let it flow out of you.

→ 10 minutes of yoga or a walk.

→ Drink water (warm water w/ lemon is great).

→ Eat a healthy breakfast.

→ Read for 15-20 minutes.

→ Avoid the news for the first 2 hours of the day.

Activity: Reframing Limiting Beliefs

It is time to rewrite those beliefs into more positive, empowering ones. What belief is the opposite of your limiting belief? For the limiting beliefs you have identified, rewrite them into something that is more aligned with the person you want to be.

- E.G. Limiting Belief: I can't make money.
- New Belief: I am worthy.

Limiting Belief	Empowering Belief

What is your biggest challenge? How has it helped you? How did you overcome it?

_____

What is your biggest fear? How has it helped you?

What is the next challenge/fear/belief that you want to overcome? How will your life change for the better as a result?

In the space below, write the following statements big and bold:

→ I AM CAPABLE OF ACHIEVING MY GOALS AND DREAMS!
→ I AM WORTHY OF SUCCESS!
→ I AM ENOUGH!

A Brief Intermission

Before we move on, it's time for some reflection. Write down any events, feelings, thoughts, people, or memories that have come up for you up to this point. There is space here to get you started, but you might want to journal more on these later.

Do not stop to think or edit yourself here. Just get pen to paper and let whatever needs to flow out of you come out. You can then repeat the steps above for each situation or person or thing that comes up. You do not need to do it all at once, even though I recognize that it is tempting to do so.

As you go through this, it will likely feel uncomfortable. Because of this, you might feel the urge to try to clear everything out as fast as possible, or avoid it altogether. Give yourself time to feel the emotions. Let yourself process it. Remember that healing and releasing can be exhausting, so be gentle with yourself! Let yourself feel what you need to, and then you can let it go.

Work through one scenario at a time. That can help prevent the feeling of overwhelm. Once you feel as though you have gotten it all out, go do something fun...something that feels good. Then come back and revisit the activity again in a day or so, when you are well-rested. This gives creates space for more fun and a sense of freedom to take hold in your life. You can start to implement all that you have learned so far.

Some things to consider:

> What revelations have you had?
> How do you feel?
> Is there something you would like to say to someone that you have been holding onto?
> Is there something you want to tell yourself?

Dear Self,

_____

_____

_____

_____

_____

_____

_____

_____

_____

_____

_____

_____

_____

_____

_____

_____

_____

_____

_____

_____

_____

_____

_____

_____

Love, Yourself

To make changes in your life – to take risks, to create something new – involves risk. Understanding the energy of that is not enough. We need to also love ourselves enough to take the journey, going where our energy takes us. Without self-love, there is doubt, fear, hesitation, resistance. It becomes a start-stop/push-pull struggle to get things done. We are living with the energy of our past, of other people, and of the expectations that were put upon us by other people.

BUT...

When you love yourself enough, you stand and tall and proud of who you are. You are confident and empowered. You hear your intuition, loud and clear, and you follow that guidance, no matter what, trusting that it is going to take you exactly where you need to be. You and your energy need to be a priority. Remember that we receive information through both our physical and energetic senses - what your brain sees around you, and what your energetic body perceives. When you think up an idea that you feel is the right next action for you, you tune into your heart space to receive the guidance on where to put your energy to bring that idea to life. If you walk around, day to day, not taking care of yourself, not loving yourself, not caring for yourself, your time, energy, and personal resources get allocated to the wrong things – things that don't really make sense for what you really, truly want.

Remember that YOU are the key to your own success and happiness. By putting yourself on the back burner, you negatively impact your own goals and dreams and desires. It's like telling the universe "yah...I am not really all that worthy of getting what I want..." That feels pretty darn crummy, and gets us to a point of burnout before we have even really gotten started doing anything.

Connect with your heart space and love who we are - right now! Act in a way that makes you happy – right now! The NOW is the key word!

Energetically, when we sit back and wait for something to happen, and believe that we are only good enough or smart enough or successful enough once we have it, we are telling the universe "hold on...I am not ready for this yet...I don't deserve it." Because remember – like attracts like from an energetic standpoint.

Self-Care and Self-Acceptance: What's the Difference?

Self-care is the most important thing we can do in our lives, regardless of whether or not we are on a track to transformation. Self-care is about giving ourselves the time and space to take care of ourselves, mentally, emotionally, physically, spiritually. Often times, we associate self-care with things like manicures, massages, and trips to the spa. Yes, these can be part of any self-care routine. Self-care also looks like: getting to the gym, sitting in nature, reading a book, taking a nap, eating nutritious foods...things that we can do to take care of us, individually.

Each of us has a different set of needs, and a different threshold for the amount of stress our systems can take on before we feel run down and burn out. When we practice good self-care rituals, we provide tools to reset when we need it, so that our times feeling run down don't last too long, and we can get back to working towards our goals. The nice thing is: we don't need to wait until we feel worn out to practice self-care, and the sad thing is, we somehow have created a culture that has adopted this very hard, sad myth. Do not wait until you feel burn-out to take that mental health day and practice self-care. Instead, incorporate good self-care practices into your life each day to better manage the day-to-day stress.

To practice self-care, we often need to go back to the basics and:

> ➤ Listen to our bodies. What foods do you want to eat? What clothes feel good? Do you need more water? Sleep? Exercise?
> ➤ Take breaks from work and move/stretch.
> ➤ Put the phone down and connect to yourself or others, or do something creative.
> ➤ Eating healthily, but sometimes indulge in your favorite foods.
> ➤ Taking time to get into nature.
> ➤ Allow ourselves to play and have fun – however that looks for us, individually.
> ➤ Go get the massage, manicure, or new hair-do. Don't wait! Schedule it now!

Self-acceptance, on the other hand, is a state of appreciation for who you are. You accept yourself for the person you are, right now, in this moment...not who you were yesterday or last week, and not who you are working towards becoming. When you accept yourself, you do not settle for less than you deserve – physically, emotionally, spiritually, and energetically. You have a high regard for your needs and your own well-being, and you know what you need to do to make sure your needs are met.

The beautiful thing is: when you accept yourself, you are also more likely to be accepting and tolerant of other people. You come to a point in your journey where you realize that: if you are doing the best you can, and you allow yourself to have those flaws and imperfections, then the same goes for other people, too. It's not about excusing bad behavior, or allowing people to take advantage of us. Instead, we accept ourselves, know what we will tolerate and what we won't, which creates space for other people to do the same. We get to choose if there's a synergy, an energetic match, between the two. If not, if things feel off, we can choose to walk away or stay, accepting the situation and the other person for who and what it is right now.

Life is a fine balance between taking care of yourself and serving others. If you give and give and give and don't look after yourself, you'll crash and burn. Setting boundaries and creating a structure and framework for your life that feels good gets you where you want to be and supports everything you want. That feels freaking fantastic!

To cultivate self-acceptance:

> Talking to and about yourself with love
> Prioritizing yourself
> Giving yourself a break from self-judgement
> Trusting yourself
> Being true to yourself
> Being nice to yourself
> Setting healthy boundaries
> Forgiving yourself when you aren't being true or nice to yourself
> Take actions based on your needs, rather than your wants
> Forgive others

If you want to change your story, start by loving yourself. Love your journey – who you are and where you have been. Accept what has happened in the past good, bad, different, mistakes and all. Choose to love yourself anyway. It's in the past. You can't change it. Acknowledge that you tried your best based on the experience and information you had at the time. Now, you know better – choose better!

Self-love and self-acceptance are motivators to make positive choices in your life, choices that support your growth and leave you feeling good. Self-love influences a lot, like: who you choose to befriend or date, the career you choose, how you cope with problems. It is a state of appreciation for all that you are – right now! Not who you intend to be later.

Keep in mind that, though close, self-acceptance is not the same thing as self-esteem. Acceptance is an acknowledgement of who you are. Self-esteem refers to how you feel about yourself. When you accept yourself, it becomes easier to feel good about yourself, but understand that they are not the same thing.

"When you love yourself, you make a conscious decision to do whatever is in your best interest to make yourself happy, healthy, and living an authentic life."
– Elizabeth Miles

Self-Acceptance: An Activity

For this exercise, you will need a mirror, your notebook, and a timer.

> ➢ Set the timer for 5 minutes.
> ➢ Take a minute to breathe.
> ➢ Look at yourself in the mirror. Acknowledge who you see in front of you.

What aspects of yourself can you accept? Which do you have trouble accepting? Take some notes here, and then go back to your notebook later and write any additional thoughts or feelings back this.

The goal: look at yourself and accept all of what you see. You don't need to change anything. There are no excuses, or feelings of anger or shame, and you don't see any flaws. You see what's there, and can let the reflection be as it is.

When the timer goes off, continue writing in about this experience in your journal.

What does 'self-love' and 'self-care' mean to you?

Who taught you about self-care? What was that message?

What does it mean to "put yourself first"? Is it right or wrong to you to do this? Why? What images or words come to mind?

Do you ever find yourself making excuses as to why you don't have time for yourself? What are they?

How would life look and feel different if you didn't make those excuses?

Do you know someone who is really good at putting him/herself first? Describe how they do this and how you feel about it.

_____

What are some of your favorite self-care activities? How regularly do you do them?

_____

What needs to change for you to start putting yourself and your needs first? Are you willing to commit to that?

What do you currently love or admire about yourself?

What do you need to do to be more at peace with yourself?

What gives me energy? Who or What inspires me?

Have I ever valued the opinion of someone else more than my own? Why?

How do you feel about yourself?

For what do you judge yourself? What do you need to tell yourself to accept the situation(s), despite any mistakes or flaws?

Fill in the blanks...I am ready to stop
_____ in order to make others like me,
and I am ready to start doing _____
because they are good for me.

What would your younger self be proud of you for right now?

Forgiveness

Let's face it – we all make mistakes – against ourselves and others. When something goes down...and you have likely had this happen...someone said or did something that hurt you. Suddenly, that relationship that was so near and dear to us for so long is damaged, or maybe even completely broken.

If we are going to talk about acceptance and self-love, we also need to spend some time talking about forgiveness. Because, when these unfortunate situations occur, they don't feel good. We get uncomfortable, hurt, sad, and angry. Other people get uncomfortable, and might have similar responses.

Forgiveness is an action word. It's a conscious choice to let go of any anger or resentment toward someone who has hurt you – even if they don't deserve it. Forgiveness does not mean that the offensive behavior was okay. We can choose to forgive the person, without excusing the act. And, forgiveness doesn't obligate you to reconcile with the person who harmed you, or release them from accountability. Instead, forgiveness is the act of releasing the energetic attachment to the situation, the actions, and the words that hurt us in the first place.

Remember back to the section on energy. Everything is energy, including the hurtful things we do or say to other people. And, with that, also remember that we hold onto the energy inside of us. That said, we hold onto the energy of the crap that happens in our lives. The energy of all the ways you were hurt by someone else at any point in your life is still lingering inside of you, unless you make the choice and effort to let it go and forgive them.

Forgiveness clears that negative energy so that you have more space for something more positive. It doesn't have to be part of your story, and it doesn't have to define you. Maybe you will choose to never speak to that person again - that's okay. That is your choice. The point is: you can accept what happened, understand the lesson it taught you, and then move forward, without the emotional attachment, making new choices that align better with what you want and who you are.

Often, we do things or say things that make us angry with ourselves. It's just as important to forgive ourselves as it is to forgive other people. Nobody is perfect!

Here's the thing, though...when we get angry, or hurt, usually, it means we are afraid. Afraid of what we will lose, afraid we will be judged, afraid we will be alone. This fear causes us to avoid movement forward. We tell ourselves that we can't/shouldn't/won't do something, and we convince ourselves that the story we are telling ourselves is true, forgetting that the root cause is fear.

Interestingly enough, ego kicks in here, in high gear, and says something like:

> Someone else made me feel bad.
> Someone else was angry or made me angry.
> It wasn't my fault, because...
> I can't do it because something else did _____ and made me feel _____.
> Excuses, excuses, excuses!

Because, let's face it – nobody wants to admit when they were wrong. By admitting any personal accountability, it means we aren't perfect. It means we are vulnerable. And it means that, maybe someone else will see us as less-than-perfect, too. This is a scary proposition.

Forgiveness is key!

Why should I forgive someone who hurt me? Why is it important?

Should others forgive you? Why or why not?

What is the relationship between love and forgiveness? Can you truly act out of love (yourself, others, your life) if there is no forgiveness?

Whom do I need to forgive in my life? For what? What would like feel like if I wasn't holding onto that resentment?

What is your initial reaction to the concept of forgiveness? Do you react in denial, anger, blame, or judgment? Do you perhaps feel hostile toward the whole idea of forgiveness as a necessity?

What characteristics in your life might indicate that you haven't fully forgiven past hurts, even if you know in your head what you need to do?

Why have you found it difficult to forgive in the past?

Values and Boundaries and Priorities, Oh My!

- ✓ Do your values and priorities align with your energy and mindset?
- ✓ Do you set boundaries that align with your values and priorities?

Values are very broad categories for goals for our life, things we desire that bring us a sense of fulfillment, joy, and happiness. They are a critical piece of who you are and they're the principles that you follow in your own life.

Priorities help you decide which goals you focus on, and in what order. This guides your actions. As an example: If you say you value health, you prioritize your time and energy to match that value – get to the gym, eat well, etc.

Boundaries are the limits we set with other people or ourselves, what we find acceptable or unacceptable, what we will tolerate. To set boundaries, we have to know ourselves – what feels good to us, what doesn't, and what we value. Upholding boundaries is just as important as setting them. When someone crosses one of our boundaries, they are admitting to you "hey there – yah, your boundaries don't matter, and I am going to walk all over you." If you don't uphold your boundaries, you will be taken advantage of. So, there should be consequences when boundaries are violated.

Remember that we teach people how to treat us. If we continuously allowing a boundary breach to occur, we're showing the people around us that it's okay for them to treat us this way. By setting and upholding our boundaries, we show others what we're allowing and not allowing to occur in our life. Along with this, understand: if other people are not used to you holding the line, it's going to make them uncomfortable the minute you act on this new behavior. Prepare for this. Make sure that, as you think through and set your boundaries, you are ready for that discomfort to happen, and can plan your communication accordingly.

If we don't learn to set healthy boundaries, we find ourselves run down, burnt out, and overwhelmed. This is no fun. When we face boundary issues in life or business, it's typically because our core values have been violated or breached in some way. So before establishing your boundaries, let's identify your core values.

Know your values! Become aware of how you are prioritizing your life. Commit to your boundaries.

Keep in mind: how do you want to feel? This feeling propels you to take action.

Some examples of values:

Abundance	Accomplishment	Adventure	Calm	Education	Hope
Confident	Creative	Empowered	Fulfilled	Certainty	Recognition
Strength	Health	Mindfulness	Awareness	Hard work	Organization
Refreshed	Optimism	Satisfaction	Thankful	Spontaneity	Independence
Beauty	Love	Motivation	Peace	Freedom	Joy
Valuable	Intelligence	Integrity	Honesty	Loyalty	Happiness

Which words resonate with you the most when you think about priorities and values? Write them below. Are there any others?

When you achieve your goals, how do you intend to feel?

Why is it important to you that you feel this way?

Do you believe that you deserve to have these in your life? Why or why not?

List 3 people that you really admire and look up to. What is it about these people that stand out to you? What do you admire?

How do you see these people upholding their boundaries?

What do you spend your money on? Is this in line with your values? How about your goals?

What do you have scheduled in your calendar for the next month? Where do you spend your time? Is this in line with your values and goals?

What words came up the most in your answers to the previous questions? What patterns are you noticing?

Now, ask yourself: are these true for me or values I adopted? Is this how I want to continue? Which values do I want to keep, and which do I want to let go of?

Using this information, what are the non-negotiables for you in your life?

Think back to the last time you were mad or upset – what values were being violated that caused you to feel this way?

What relationships stick out in your mind that currently do not feel good? What is it about this relationship that triggers you? Are your boundaries being violated? How?

What boundaries would you like to set for your life? Why? Can you commit to starting now?

How will you handle things when your boundaries are violated? What will the consequences be?

Confidence

Confidence comes at the intersection of a positive mindset, accepting and loving yourself, and believing in your abilities, skills, and talents. Without having even the slightest amount of confidence in your ability to achieve anything, and without a positive mindset or self-acceptance, action becomes a challenge. After all, why bother moving forward if you believe, with certainty that you will fail? And why take any action to move ahead if you don't believe that you are good enough to do it?

Trust me – no matter how many times you believe you have failed in the past, you are still capable – and worthy – of change, of moving forward, and of achieving whatever it is you really want.

And it isn't arrogant or rude to believe that.

We are all here for a purpose. There is a reason that you are alive right now, and you have a unique gift to bring to the world. It's okay to feel the value of who you are in this world. It's okay to feel good about yourself. If nobody else has ever told you that in the past, let me be the first, and I will repeat it:

> ➤ It's okay to feel good about yourself!
> ➤ It's okay to have dreams!
> ➤ It's okay to go after them!
> ➤ It's okay to achieve them!
> ➤ It's okay to live an abundant life!

This is something that I struggled with for a long time. I believed that, if I achieved my goals, and was excited about it, I was being boastful, braggy, and arrogant, and would make other people feel bad. I had to take a look at that mindset and the beliefs around it, following the energy back clear away the blocks from my childhood. What I realized is:

- There is a major difference between wanting to improve my life for my own sake, and because it feels right and good for me, and wanting to succeed to one-up the person next to me. Life is not a competition. There are no winners or losers.
- There is choice, decision, action, and belief, and following the energy of those towards what feels best for me.
- I can achieve my goals and be happy for myself, and celebrate that success. It might upset someone else to see or hear about that accomplishment, but that is not something I can control. Their response is for them to look at and change, if they choose, and is not something I need to concern my time, energy, or resources trying to fix or change. And it is certainly not an excuse to hide or live small or restricted.

That said, I also don't have to walk around acting and talking like I am better than anyone else because of my accomplishments. That is slimy and feels icky. Every individual is capable and deserving of success. Just because one person "gets there" and someone else doesn't, does not make any one individual better or worse. Just like we are all here for a purpose we all have lessons we need to learn, things we need to overcome. We all have challenges and obstacles. Nobody is any better than anyone else, and the size of one's house or bank account does not determine value or worth. Neither does the number of followers on social media, number of friends someone has, or the job or tasks they perform at their job.

We want those feelings of confidence, abundance, and success to be so strong and so clear for us. They are things we crave, but we believe that we have to wait to have them before we can do anything else. Then, we assign labels and values from the outside world to determine our worth. This stops us from doing anything at all, because we end up looking around at the world around us, and assigning what the value of success and abundance means, based on what we see someone else having or doing or being.

This is why it's important to see and feel confident NOW! To understand our mindset NOW! To love ourselves NOW! ... Because feeling and believing these NOW put us in a state where we know that we are okay, we know that, while we might not have it all figured out (yet), we are headed in the right direction, and we are going to create a life that feels good to us, no matter what!

The Universe is an abundant place. There is plenty here for everyone. Abundance and success mean different things to each person, and everyone is worthy of achieving the levels of abundance and success they choose.

"Beauty begins the moment you decided to be yourself."
COCO CHANEL

What does confidence mean to you?

Was there a time in your life when you felt truly confident? Where were you? Hold old? Who was with you? What was happening?

What would it take to feel that level of confidence again?

Are you willing to commit to yourself to take those steps?

What accomplishments are you MOST proud of?

What challenges have you had to overcome to get where you are today?

What are the top 5 most difficult situations that you've endured and overcome in your life?

In what ways have you improved your life, or the lives of others?

Why do other people tell you that you are amazing?

What does success mean to you?

What is "abundance"?

Use this space to write about what you think makes you a great person. Save this and reflect on them when you need a confidence boost - when you need a reminder as to why you're doing what you're doing. These are all the reasons why people relate to you and are energetically attracted to you.

Ego v. Intuition: The Battle of the Ages

Have you ever found yourself saying "I should have followed my gut" or "I knew that was going to happen" or "I know it's going to work out" or "I have no idea why I feel so compelled to do so, but I am going to take a different route to work today."

...These are all words of your intuition.

Intuition refers to those non-logical, non-analytical, hard-to-quantify bits of knowledge that somehow seem to speak to us, and guide us through life. Intuition is, basically, a hunch, and, often, hard to quantify or define. It's that "sense" that something is right or wrong, good or bad, even when there are no hard facts to back that up. Your intuition is an inner teacher or guide, there to keep you on the right track. It is constantly scanning and reading the energy around you and then speaks to you, in a very particular and personal way, to let you know the next steps for you to take. It's more of a gentle, soft nudge or whisper.

On the flip side, have you ever said to yourself: "you're crazy" or "what the hell was that guy thinking by cutting me off in traffic" or "there's never enough time/money"?

...This is all ego.

The ego is that voice that, usually, is the first and loudest to speak when we are sitting quietly by ourselves. It's the voice of blame, shame, denial, control, judgement, maybe even victimization. Your ego is responsible for analyzing your reality, or the data the world presents to you. It exists to ensure you survive, have enough food, making sure your environment is safe. It's loud, sometimes obnoxious, hurtful, maybe even overbearing.

The ego and your intuition will often sound somewhat similar. But they function in very different ways.

The ego is part of your physical body, part of your brain that keeps you stuck in the past, recalling memories to remind you to act differently in the future. It keeps you on guard. It's very analytical.

Your intuition, on the other hand, exists in your energetic body, and presents itself through the five senses. It's generally pushing you in the direction that you want to go in life.

For example, if you were to ask yourself, "Should I devote more time to more hobbies?"... Your intuition would respond immediately with a "yes" and a few moments later the ego would come in and list all the reasons why it's not a good idea.

Trusting your intuition is not easy. Sometimes it tells us something that we don't understand. It doesn't always make sense. It can make us uncomfortable. Our intuition challenges us to take action. To follow our dreams. To take the next step. It also challenges us to look at what makes us uncomfortable. What isn't working? What needs to change? It's like a muscle that needs exercise in order to strengthen it, and when you are engaging in activities that support your wellbeing – i.e. getting enough rest, getting proper nutrition...all the self-love – you can better manage your energy, and, therefore, will have an easier time discerning the voice of the ego versus the vice of your intuition. You'll have an easier time recognizing what feels good and what does not. This way, when your intuition is telling you "nope, that's not the right thing" you will hear, listen, trust, and then act accordingly. You learn to find that balance between walking on the edge of what is comfortable and what is outside of the comfort zone.

This process is continuously changing and evolving. Your inspiration and actions come from your intuition. The most essential thing to remember here, is to ACT on your inspired ideas immediately. This ensures that you do not give your ego any time to come in and say, "No that's not a good idea, don't do that!" or any other unpleasant thoughts! Once you have set the intention for what you are calling into your life, the universe is sending you the inspiration to get what you want. It is your job to act.

It is important to focus your energy on the things that you know are working. Putting your energy into tasks that you believe you "should do" because someone else told you that it worked for them is draining your energy. Stop doing those things and focus your energy where it counts. This will free up time for you to enjoy life, work less - making time for self-care - so you can stay in tune with your intuition.

How we perceive intuitive information is different for everyone. Many may have 1 or 2 dominate, intuitive traits. The fun and interesting thing to note is: you can develop any of these at any time. Your intuition communicates through the following means:

> Sight - Images you see in your mind's eye and in your dreams.
> Hearing - Clear thoughts and words that you hear in your mind that feel grounded and inspired, songs that come into your head, etc. These thoughts do not come from a "busy" mind, but from somewhere deep down inside you.
> Feeling - Bodily sensations are one of the most powerful intuitive senses and come in many forms, such as a knowing in your gut, or feelings of anxiety or illness when something is not right.
> Smell and Taste - Some people have the nose for truth or following hunches.
> Your intuition gives you information, ideas, impressions. Any time you get a feeling, or any time an idea pops into your head, even the ones that seem crazy and random – that is the voice of your intuition. You might have random knowledge of things that you would not normally know about.

When we are not following our intuition, our bodies tend to feel heavy, dense, maybe there is an uncomfortable knot in the pit of our stomach. Things do not feel good. On the other hand, when we are following the guidance, we tend to feel light, free, and expansive. Manage your energy and take this in baby steps, allowing yourself the time and practice to really understand your intuition. There is no one, single, best or right way to do anything. There is, however, the intuitive way. So, listen to yourself. Do what feels right. Always!

"A bad day for your ego, is a great day for your soul."

– Jillian Michaels

How to Listen to Your Intuition

- Pay attention to how your body feels when you're making decisions.
- Does your stomach feel tight?
- Do you feel excited?
- Do you get negative feelings when you have to go to a specific place or connect with certain people?
- Listen to the words that pop into your head (they are trying to tell you something!).
- Even songs in your mind can have messages for you. Write them down before they go away.
- Be aware of images that appear in your mind's eye, or dreams you have at night, even if it's just a quick picture in your head. They are divine downloads.
- Act on those feelings that don't go away - even if it seems trivial (i.e. take a dance class, eat more bananas, etc.). That's your intuition guiding you.
- Have faith! Remind yourself that guidance is coming and everything you need to know will be revealed in time. Your ego is the part of you controlling that urge to get all the answers NOW, and do everything NOW. Life doesn't have to be that chaos-driven.

The stronger our intuition gets, the calmer and more guided we feel. There is a sense of peace knowing that, no matter what situation we find ourselves, we will be able to navigate our way through. A word of caution though: without taking the time to understand our energy, our thoughts, and our emotions, listening to our intuition can be tricky. Remember: Ego pops up to keep us safe, which lends itself to fear. That fear might sound like our intuition. Over time, you will get more comfortable knowing the difference.

What becomes important is:

> ➤ Paying attention to your surroundings.
> ➤ Noticing the energy around you and how it feels.
> ➤ Connecting that with how you think and feel.

Often, we notice when we haven't listened to our intuition – you know those moments when you sit back, slap yourself on the forehead and go "I just knew it!"

We have all had those moments. Take those as proof that you truly have intuitive skills. In reality, the more you use your intuition the stronger it becomes. But it doesn't always speak clearly or loudly. This is where faith and trust come in, but the more you work on this, the easier it becomes to listen and trust. Your intuition will never steer you wrong.

Remember that, when you tap into your intuition, the answers might not be clear. If it's truly your intuition, this will be temporary, and the messages will make more sense in the future. Write down what you hear, see, or feel, to keep track.

Activity: Getting in Touch with Intuition

To get in touch with our intuition, we are going to start by focusing on things that both feel good, and do not feel good, for us. Using the boxes below, make a list of 10 things that feel good to you and then 10 things that do not feel good. These can be anything...your favorite sweater, the smell of freshly-brewed coffee, the feeling of a warm breeze on your skin. The key is to connect these things with how they make you feel.

Feels Good	Feels Bad

Why is it important to connect with what feels good and what feels bad? Why should we care how daily activities feel for us? ... Great question!

Remember: our intuitive guidance will likely feel light, free, and airy and guidance that is ego-driven will likely feel heavy. This is not limited to things. It also extends to people, places, activities, basically, everything we do or interact with. When we connect with the energy of what feels good for us, versus what feels bad, we will have an easier time trusting the voice of our intuition, which is feeding us messages all the time. If we are not in the habit of listening and following the guidance, we are likely to miss our next steps. Having mindful awareness for what feels good and what feels bad is going to be the first step in learning how our intuition speaks to us.

Your intuition is important. Trusting your gut feeling will never lead you down the wrong path. To get what you want, to live your purpose, listen to the guidance from your intuition, and then take the action steps it provides. That is not always easy, because intuition does not necessarily give us steps that make logical sense to us at the time. Because of this, fear and resistance tend to kick in and tell us our intuition is wrong. Mindful awareness of our energy is important. Fear is going to feel heavy and dense, while intuition feels light. When you are aware of this, it becomes easier to challenge yourself. Then, you can continue the process to understand what works, what does not, and what changes you need to make.

Activity: Seeking An Intuitive Answer

What clarity do you need? What questions do you have? Take some time to listen to the voice and guidance of your intuition. If it's helpful, write your question at the top of a piece of paper to give you more focus.

- ➢ Sit quietly and take a few deep breaths. Tell yourself that you are open to receiving guidance.
- ➢ First, a brain dump to tune into your logical mind.
  - o In order to tune into your more logical sided brain, you have to ask the questions-
    - ▪ What does my mind say?
    - ▪ What does my fear say?
  - o In your notebook, take some time to write these answers down. It doesn't matter what that information actually is. Your ego has something to say – it always does. In order to get in touch with your intuition, you want to give yourself some time to dump all that ego out.
  - o After dumping the contents of your mind, it will help you to switch over to your intuition. In order to do this you need to bring your attention to the present moment.
- ➢ Ask your intuition to speak to you.
  - o Do you have other questions you'd like clarity on about this situation?
  - o Try to keep it clear and succinct as this will help you to receive the clearest answer.
  - o What answers come through? Do you:
    - ▪ Hear song lyrics in your mind? Or pieces of a poem?
    - ▪ Does a color come to mind?
    - ▪ Do you see a vision of your answer?
    - ▪ Do you hear a voice with your answer?
    - ▪ Do you get a sense of hot or cold?
- ➢ Bring yourself back to the present moment.

If you don't receive an answer straight away, or you unsure about your answer, try sitting with your question and wait for the answer to come. Don't try to push it, but instead flow with the energy that is around you.

Over time the more you repeat this exercise, the stronger your intuition will become.

Another Intuitive Exercise

Get comfortable, close your eyes, and then take a few slow, deep breaths.

→ Focus your attention on your breath as it goes in... and then out.

→ Imagine all of the tension leaving your body with each exhalation.

→ Continue doing this until you start to feel calm and relaxed.

→ Next, think about an area of your life that you would like guidance or clarity on and form a question that could shed light on it.

→ Be open to the guidance.

→ As you ask your question, notice any sensations in your body – feelings, images, or thoughts.

Some examples of the types of questions you could ask:

➢ "What is really going on with _____?"

➢ "What do I need to know about _____?"

➢ "Why do I feel stuck / confused / blocked?"

➢ "How can I improve this situation?"

➢ "What is the best course of action to take regarding _____?"

➢ "Is there something that I am missing or not seeing? If so, what is it?"

How do you feel that your intuition communicates with you now? What intuitive hunches have you gotten recently?

Are you listening to your intuition? Think about how have you been spending your time? What activities do you do on a daily, weekly, or monthly basis?

Are there activities that you are spending your time on that are not necessarily related to your goals, but you continue to do because you were taught that you needed to be responsible for them? What does your intuition tell you about these activities?

What things make you feel completely drained? These are likely the ones that are not working or you and will continue to be an issue moving forward. Why are you still doing these things?

What aspects of your current life situation are not fully in alignment with your true self? In other words, what "feels bad" for you?

What would it look and feel like to be living in authenticity every day?

What specific things would you be doing to fulfill your life purpose? What things would you like to do more of, simply because it feels good and makes you happy?

Think back to the beginning of the workbook and the talents and skills you listed. Do you have any that you want to develop? What does your intuition tell you that you need to do to begin developing these? Do you need to enroll in anything? Buy a book? Etc.?

Activity: A Meditation

We have spent a lot of time focusing on our mindset, our energy, and our intuition. Now, we are going to take all of that and use it to set some goals. Before we get started, let's sit in the vibration of how we want to feel.

> - Set a timer for 10 minutes.
> - Then, sit with your eyes closed and breathe. Focus on the breath moving into your heart.
> - Think about what you want to feel each day. Is it: Love? Fulfilled? Success? Happiness? Gratitude? Something else entirely?
> - Where does that feel in your body?
> - Get clear on your WHY, your purpose, your mission. Create a crystal-clear vision for yourself, along with your goals. How do you want to show up in the world? What message do you want to convey? What legacy do you want to leave?
> - Focus on tasks that align with your purpose and goals for your life. If it does not align with either, then it is using valuable resources (I.e. time, energy, focus), which sets you back further from achieving your goals.

Manifestation, Co-Creation, and
Intuitive Goal-Setting

How do you want to change your life?

We all have things we want in life. Some of us want a better body, or more money. Others want romance. Maybe we tell ourselves we want to be successful. In life, goals are important. They give us something to work towards, aspire to. They keep us growing and evolving. Enter manifestation and co-creation...thank you Universe and Law of Attraction! You've gotten to the point where you've placed your order with the Universe and now you're anticipating what's to come. How will you get where you want to go? What will happen next? Co-creation and manifestation are fun and exciting because, when you make a request of the Universe, each day becomes one big mystery. You aren't quite sure how things are going to shake out!

Here's the thing...try as hard as you want - you can't control the "how!"

Your ego is going to want to rationalize and control the process of how you arrive your chosen destination. It's going to look at everyone and everything else around you as evidence to support or discourage your path. The key to this section is to follow your intuition and take the steps you are given. The Universe works very hard to get you where you want to go, but it likes a little action on your part. In order for it to get you there, you need to be heavily involved. Help the Universe to help you.

By following your intuition no matter what, you are strengthening your spiritual connection as well as building your confidence to trust what your intuition is telling you to do. Intuition is how the Universe speaks to us, so the more you follow it, the louder it becomes!

Following your intuition can mean: anything that you are drawn or called to do, say, go, follow, make, walk into, or drive in a certain direction. Stay open to any and all possibilities. You'll be surprised at how often you meet the right people or find a path that leads you to something completely unexpected and magical!

The point is: when you understand your mindset, recognize the beliefs that stop you from taking action, and you have a keen awareness for what you really want, you have to commit to taking inspired action to create the change you want to see. You'll receive intuitive guidance and ideas regularly that will help you get closer and closer to these goals. The not-so-great news is: not all goals are created equal. We tend to start out by telling ourselves something like "I want to change my life" and, while this has the best of intentions, it's not very specific, and can feel pretty daunting and overwhelming. Taking the time to focus on what we want, getting as specific as possible on those key areas we want to impact is more helpful for us in the long-term, and short-term. We can better take actionable steps right now, with the vision of where those steps are leading.

Notice, we are putting the statement above in the present tense. This gets us out of the mindset that we don't have what we desire. We want to get ourselves in a mindset of action. Reminding yourself that you might not yet have what you want tends to create feelings of lack, limitation, sometimes stalling. We want to reinforce that you can, and DO, achieve your goals, not that you will, or might. It's time to make it a certainty, an absolute that you feel this way.

6-Week Goals

What are your primary goals for the next six weeks? If you could wave a magic wand and have everything work out exactly as you intended...Who do you want to be six weeks from now? What will have changed between now and then?

6-Month Goals

What are your primary goals for the next six months? What will you have accomplished? How do you feel you are evolving? What habits have fallen away and which ones have you adopted? What feels different? There are no limits here, so make it something that feels really good to you.

12-Month Goals

What are your primary goals for the next twelve months? Who do you want to be one year from now? What will you have accomplished? What do your surroundings look like? What do you think and believe? Write about it here. This is your vision, so dream big, and make it really juicy! No limits, remember!

Alignment and Vision

We all have things we want to accomplish, goals we want to achieve. It's easy to make a list and say "these are my goals" - but do nothing to take the steps forward to make them happen. When this occurs, your goals are a wish list. To help move ourselves along, we want to create a compelling vision. Something positive, personal, and something that you can see, with crystal clarity.

Why?

When you can see your desired life, you can also feel what it feels like, and then follow the energy to bring it to you. When you sit with a vision that feels so good and fun and authentic to you, your mind is open, and it is easier to see possibilities and take action. It is much easier, from this place of authenticity and feeling good, that you listen to your heart and give it what it really wants.

And, let's face it! It's a lot easier to motivate ourselves to move when we feel good. You can better focus your time, attention, energy, and resources in the direction of your goals.

So, what do you want? Does it align with your priorities and values? Are you confident in your ability to get there?

How do you want to feel? Remember the feelings that you associated with your values a few pages back? These are core desired feelings. At the core of who you are, this is how you want to feel when all of your needs are met. They should align with your values.

For example:

If you value hard work, you desire to feel fulfilled in life.

If you value family, your core desire is connection.

What do you do that makes you feel your core desired feelings? Is it curling up with a good book? Exercise? Painting or drawing? There is no right or wrong answer. The goal is to regularly get yourself into these feelings NOW. Essentially, you are calling the feelings you want to feel in the future and saying "hey, let's hang out now."

The more you do these, the faster you can manifest things into your life. Why? Because they keep you feeling good. You are prioritizing yourself, your needs, and your feelings above everything else. This is an act of self-love. Beyond that, think back to some of section on energy. Like attracts like. When you are looking to attract good things to you, do so from a place of feeling that same goodness, as if you already had those things in your life now.

How often are you doing these things you've listed above? Be honest with yourself. Are you making these a priority?

Arrange your calendar so that you have the time set aside to dedicate to you! Set boundaries, so that the people around you know that, when that time comes around, it's yours. And let them know why it's important to you to have that time. In this way, we can be an example for other people, and let them know that it is okay for them to have healthy boundaries, too.

Try to do something every single day, but at an absolute minimum, set time for yourself at least once per week to make sure you're doing one or more of these actions.

Life is way more fun when we are doing things we like to do.

It's easy to get sidetracked in life. It's easy to allow ourselves to give into distraction. When we don't have a clear, compelling vision, and we don't know what we want to feel, or what we need to do, it's easy to get overwhelmed and lost in that feeling of being stuck. And it is easy to let excuses run our life. It is also easy to avoid boundaries, because we get afraid that, by having them, we are going to upset other people in the process.

Your life, your dreams, your goals all need to be a priority if you are going to move forward. You likely have a ton of other responsibilities – kids, work, family, etc. I know – life happens! This is why we need to know what we want, why we want it, and what we want our life to feel like. And we need to be okay setting boundaries and asking for help, so that we can use our time, energy, and resources to achieve all of that.

One other thing that I learned over time:

By delegating, asking for help, and setting boundaries, it helps other people step up and learn and grow, too. You make it okay for them to be someone or something else. There is magic there, because the relationship becomes more fluid, peaceful, and fun. You can communicate, compromise, and negotiate from a place that feels open and safe, instead of one that is controlling, rigid, or even fake.

Activity: Create A Schedule for Success

Take some time to schedule tasks to get you moving toward your goals. You can plan your time as you need to, according to your energy, availability, outside resources. The point is: don't wait to get moving.

> ➤ Start by giving yourself a timeframe. Given your current values and priorities, and your current non-negotiable responsibilities, set a deadline for your goals.
> ➤ Next, look at what you already have on the calendar. Are there any that can be rescheduled or cancelled?
> ➤ Once you have looked over these dates and times, go back and fill individual tasks associated with each goal.

As you schedule tasks, consider the times of the day when you feel most creative or energetic. How can you prioritize tasks to complete them at these higher-energetic times? These are the periods when you will likely have an easier time focusing your attention, which will help you stay motivated, on track, and avoiding a list of half-started projects.

What will you need to do each day to keep yourself on track? For me, I had to make sure I did things like be at the gym by 6 AM, Start each day with a smoothie or protein shake, meditation or journaling, reading, meal planning for the week ahead.

Acknowledge that there are going to be days when we just don't feel like it, or when life happens, and we need to reschedule. This is OKAY. Do not beat yourself up when that happens, and don't let it keep you from continuing to make progress. Make a commitment and a plan for yourself so that, when things like these occur, you can get back on track immediately, without impeding progress.

If you are finding there are more and more days when you don't feel like it, this is something that needs to be addressed. You need to get honest with yourself and ask yourself questions like:

→ Is this resistance?

→ Where is it coming from?

→ Is this fear or nervousness?

- o Be honest with yourself so that you can work on clearing through the blocks.
- o If you find that there are more and more people, places, or things popping up preventing you from tackling your to-dos, this also needs to be addressed.
    - Why are you letting them stand in your way?
    - How can you create boundaries that benefit both sides?

What is the ultimate dream? In reality, how do you want to think, feel, and act? Take a few minutes to create that compelling vision for your life. Don't judge it. Don't try to change it or edit it. Just write and feel it.

Does this vision align with the person you want to be? Why or why not? If not, where did the vision come from?

What do you feel is holding you back from achieving the goals you set for yourself? What limiting beliefs do you need to release in order to allow yourself the permission to move forward?

Are you ready to let these beliefs go? How does this realization empower and/or inspire you to keep going?

What do you need to change & where do you need to focus to achieve your goals?

What boundaries do you need to implement to achieve the vision? How do you anticipate others will respond? How can you move past this?

What will it do for your family, and all those around you when you hit your goals?

Gratitude

One of the most powerful and transformative practices you can incorporate into your life is that of gratitude. When you are grateful, you feel more positive emotions, you can look at experiences in a more positive way, you are more likely to improve your health and overcome challenges. When you walk through life in a state of gratitude, you see the benefit to all that you have now, instead of sitting around and waiting for something good to happen.

It helps you focus on the good that is present in your life NOW, rather than focusing on the things you don't have yet. This helps foster a higher sense of self-worth and greater self-confidence. You start to see that life really is good to you, you already are successful, and are already living an abundant life!

I like to keep a notebook by my bed and start and end each day by jotting down a few things I am grateful for. Take a minute here to create your own gratitude list.

For whom or what are you grateful?

Rewriting Your Story and Wrapping Things Up

Think about the goals you laid out earlier in this workbook. What fears come up when you think about accomplishing the things you've listed above?

Where does this fear/story stem from?

What would happen if this story/fear played out? What would you do if this happened?

How likely is it that this will actually happen? Is there anything you can do to prevent it? How does this help or hinder you?

172

Re-frame this fear into a new positive story? What new messages can you send yourself, so that when that voice of fear comes back, you can stop it, and remind yourself of this new, more positive information?

Once Upon A Time...

_____

_____

_____

_____

_____

_____

_____

_____

_____

_____

_____

_____

_____

_____

_____

_____

_____

_____

_____

_____

_____

_____

What would you do if you knew failure wasn't an option and you would 100% achieve your goal? Would that change your level of belief or commitment to the goal? Why or why not?

Know this...

It doesn't matter if you are making a million or a billion dollars a year. It doesn't matter if you decide to start your own business. It doesn't matter if you choose to sell your house and travel the world in a van. It doesn't matter if you decide to go back to school, or not.

None of it matters!

All that matters is that you show up every day and act in a way that aligns with who you truly are, and who you truly want to be. If that means that, in the process, you start a business that benefits the world in some way, amazing! If that means that you make that million dollars, fantastic! I would be glad to shake your hand, give you a hug, and celebrate you.

We all have choices in life. We get to choose our thoughts, feelings, actions, and responses to the world. We get to choose if and when we are ready to let the world see our authentic face. We get to choose when we are ready to get up and step out in the world in a really big, and positive way.

Far too often, we think it's the million dollars or the entrepreneurial spirit, or the adventuresome self that will make us amazing, great, and loved, stand out.

No!

You are amazing already! You are already great. You are already love. And you already have the voice inside of you to help you stand out. All you need to do is choose it! And then, continue to choose the next right step to keep you moving in the direction that spreads your purpose and message in the most profound way.

The answers are right inside of you, and will emerge at the right time, when you allow it. There are no magic bullets, no magic beans, and no secret formulas. It comes down to you tuning in, listening to your heart, and choosing to be open and honest with yourself. This takes practice, yes! It takes time to learn and refine skills. It takes time to understand what you want and how to get it. It takes time to quiet down the messages that we have been told throughout our lives that tell us we can't/shouldn't/don't or aren't good enough. Fear feeds off of these. Become a student of life anyway. We do not need to know everything all at once. When you allow yourself to become that student, you can show yourself just what you are truly capable of achieving. You can lean into adventure and curiosity of life, and you become willing to push, with persistence and determination, to the end goal.

It is not easy to sit and examine your life. It takes courage. Acknowledge that and be proud of yourself for simply being willing to look at life from a new perspective. With each section that you complete, give yourself a minute to reflect and be proud of the work you are doing. It is okay to be proud of your progress and achievements. Allow yourself to celebrate!

Holding the vision is important! Be ready to act, and then do it! Let's face it - procrastination does not help anything. The longer you sit and wait, the more you give your brain time to think about how things can go wrong. Recognize that growth, change, and progress are not all-or-nothing. Change takes time. Growth takes time. In this case, you are going to break down the old beliefs and patterns, decide what is and is not working at this point, and then choose what you take with you in your next steps. You get to create something totally new for yourself. YOU get to choose! Use that choice to create something fun, amazing, and feels incredibly positive and perfect to YOU. Creation is done in pieces. Commit to yourself! Go all-in, and you will find success – whatever success means to you!

Activity: A Letter to You

Write a letter to yourself – your current self. Tell yourself what you think, feel, and do every day as if it has already happened in the future. What is the experience like? What has the journey been like? Don't second guess it. Don't edit it. Just write! After you finish the letter, put it away for a while. Come back to it later and read it again to get a little boost of self-esteem.

Activity: Continuous Change

Identify something about yourself that makes you feel ashamed, insecure, or just plain "not good enough." Write it down and describe how it makes you feel; be sure to identify the emotion(s) it evokes. What does the energy feel like regarding the situation? How can you apply what you have learned here to create change about this thought, belief, or situation? Think about mindset, beliefs, and energy. Think about what your intuition is telling you.

Activity: A Letter for Acceptance

Think about the situation from above. Write yourself a letter in which you show yourself compassion, understanding, and acceptance for this part of yourself that you dislike. As you write this, imagine someone who loves and accepts you unconditionally, and try to think of what that person would say to you about the part of yourself that you don't like. As you write, think about how your upbringing might have shaped this part of your life. Ask yourself what you might do to improve or cope with the situation. How can you focus on constructive changes to make yourself more fulfilled?

The End

Congratulations on making the choice to change, and ongoing on this journey with me. You now have everything you need to make the next few weeks and months a transformative period of growth and change for yourself and your life, and I hope that this process has opened the doors of personal development to you, and puts you on a track to continue on this trajectory. This is an exciting time! You are so strong, and an amazing gift to the world. Never, EVER, let anyone make you forget that.

If this was helpful to you, please share the book with someone in your life that could also use the message, or leave a review on Facebook, Amazon, Lulu, or wherever you found this book. We are all here to share our story, and create community and spread positivity together, and the more we spread this message, we march forth, stronger, more confident, living in a very authentic way. This is what the world needs more of!

I would love to hear about your insights, pivot points, and what you are working on in your life. As you move forward, don't hesitate to reach out to me. I can't wait to hear about your progress, or to help you along with questions. Email me or message me on social media. Here's where you can find me:

Website: www.marchforthmediacompany.com
Facebook: www.facebook.com/MarchForthMediaCompany
Instagram: @MarchForthMediaCo
Email: MarchForthMediaCo@gmail.com

You can also find me over on the Power to Pivot Podcast, available on Anchor, Spotify, and Apple Podcasts! Take a listen, leave a review, and share with your friends!

To Your Journey! March Forth!

With love and gratitude, *Elizabeth*

About the Author:

Elizabeth Miles is a life and business coach, and a devoted student of personal development. She is passionate about teaching clients on authentic and intuitive leadership – leading from your heart first, then using the data and metrics as a benchmark for success, no matter your path in life. Her signature program – The Intuitive MBA – is a six-month incubator for those looking to start or transform a business, taking a heart-centered, intuitive approach, rather than a logical one.

Elizabeth is the host of the Power to Pivot Podcast, where she shares insight, resources, and tools, as well as interviews others on a path looking to create positive change in the world.

Connect with Elizabeth:

Website: www.marchforthmediacompany.com
Facebook: www.facebook.com/MarchForthMediaCompany
Instagram: @MarchForthMediaCo
Email: MarchForthMediaCo@gmail.com

Also by Elizabeth A. Miles (available on Amazon, Lulu, Audible, and Barnes and Noble in paperback and digital):

→ This Is Where You Pivot: The Shift from Fear to Freedom
→ The Journey to Healing: Love, Yourself
→ The Recipe for Leadership Project: A Book on Heart-Centered Leadership for Kids

Online Courses by Elizabeth A. Miles:

→ The Energy Apprentice: A Primer for Understanding the Magic and Possibility of the Universe
→ Intuition 101: For Writers, Artists, Musicians, and Creatives Looking to Create in a More Authentic Way

Made in the USA
Middletown, DE
19 December 2020